S0-BLA-274

DRUG DOSAGE IN LABORATORY ANIMALS
A HANDBOOK

DRUG DOSAGE *in* LABORATORY ANIMALS
A HANDBOOK

by C. D. BARNES
and L. G. ELTHERINGTON

University of California Press — Berkeley and Los Angeles — 1966

UNIVERSITY OF CALIFORNIA PRESS
BERKELEY AND LOS ANGELES, CALIFORNIA
CAMBRIDGE UNIVERSITY PRESS, LONDON, ENGLAND

LIBRARY OF CONGRESS CATALOG CARD NUMBER: 64-21066
THIRD PRINTING, 1966

TO

Dr. A. Horita,

Dr. Byron A. Schottelius,

and

Dr. Orville A. Smith, Jr.

with our gratitude
and esteem

PREFACE

This handbook was conceived as a result of the authors' frustration in attempting to find appropriate drug dosage for use in laboratory animals. The few available sources of information were limited in the number of species or the routes of administration. This handbook is designed to provide a concise and up-to-date reference source of available drug dosage in seven commonly used species of laboratory animals. Parenteral and oral routes of administration are included.

We are grateful to the following individuals and firms for dosage information made available for use in this book.

DR. R. M. FEATHERSTONE, CHAIRMAN,

DEPARTMENT OF PHARMACOLOGY, UNIVERSITY OF CALIFORNIA, SAN FRANCISCO MEDICAL CENTER

DR. J. J. BOSLEY, STANFORD RESEARCH INSTITUTE

DR. B. GRAHAM, STANFORD RESEARCH INSTITUTE

ABBOTT LABORATORIES

BURROUGHS WELLCOME & CO. (U.S.A.), INC.

CHAS. PFIZER AND CO., INC.

CIBA PHARMACEUTICAL COMPANY

ELI LILLY AND COMPANY

HOFFMAN-LA ROCHE, INC.

LAKESIDE LABORATORIES, INC.

MERCK INSTITUTE

RIKER LABORATORIES, INC.

SANDOZ PHARMACEUTICALS

SCHERING CORPORATION

SMITH, KLINE AND FRENCH LABORATORIES

THE SQUIBB INSTITUTE

THE UPJOHN COMPANY

WYETH LABORATORIES

Our special thanks go to Mrs. Joan Sauer and Miss Tina Moya for their assistance in the preparation of the manuscript.

CONTENTS

INTRODUCTION

This handbook provides pharmacodynamic and toxicologic dosage information for a number of drugs commonly used in biological research. The primary consideration governing selection was that of including typical representatives of major drug groups. Chemotherapeutic agents were omitted because they exhibit little or no pharmacological activity and animal dosage information is readily obtained from package inserts which accompany veterinary preparations. Another selection criterion was that the drug had been used in a number of animal species and via more than one route of administration; some research compounds were deliberately omitted because they did not satisfy this requirement. However, a number of newer drugs, which showed promise of wide acceptance as experimental tools, were included even though they did not meet the above-mentioned criterion.

Drug responses were classified according to (1) toxicity data, (2) primary use or activity, and (3) secondary uses or activities.

In some instances, to present efficiently as much dosage information as possible, it was necessary to group a number of specific drug actions under one general heading. For example, a cardiovascular category included drug actions on cardiac rate and output and/or vascular resistance and/or mean arterial blood pressure. A behavior classification was often used to represent drug effects in conditioning and learning experiments and in experiments designed to test spontaneous motor activity. Where we had available space and sufficient references, the above drug effects were listed separately. Since the dosage entries are referenced, we felt that this technique of grouping drug responses was justified as it allowed tabulation of more information in a limited space, thus reducing the size of the handbook without sacrificing completeness.

Toxicological data were included to provide the investigator with a range of upper dosage limits for assistance in obtaining a maximally effective dose. In many instances toxicity data were obtained for a species of animal or route of administration for which no pharmacodynamic information was available. Lethal doses are presented in the following order of preference: (1) LD_{50}—amount necessary to kill 50 per cent of an experimental group; (2) MLD—minimum lethal dose, i.e., the amount sufficient to kill a single member of an experimental group; and (3) LD—that dose which has been reported to kill an unspecified number of an experimental group.

Drugs are listed in alphabetical order according to the nomenclature suggested by the World Health Organization (WHO) drug dictionary, as published in *World Neurology* of September, 1961, or the Merck Index. Whenever possible, three common names are included and cross-indexed with the official name. All *in vivo* dosages are expressed as milligrams per kilogram of body weight (mg/kg).

The introductory material, which covers factors modifying drug response and anesthesia, is a simplified, cookbook presentation of basic pharmacological principles included primarily for investigators who use drugs in their research but have little or no pharmacology background. The authors feel that, since the pharmacological literature is full of contradictory information, much of which can be explained by differences of experimental procedure and abuses of anesthetic agents or techniques, even some experienced investigators could derive benefit from the anesthesia section.

Following the section on principles of general anesthesia for acute animal experiments, a table of anesthetic agents and adjuvants is presented. This table contains a large number of single anesthetics or mixtures of agents which have been reported in the research literature.

Appendix A presents, in tabular form, hormone maintenance and replacement dosages which have been reported to be effective following surgical removal of endocrine glands. The material is completely referenced and tabulated under the surgical condition of the animal following gland removal, e.g., hypophysectomized, etc. The last page of Appendix A presents salt concentrations in grams per liter (g/L) of physiological solutions used for bathing or perfusing tissues.

In vitro concentrations, expressed as milligrams per 100 cc of bathing solution (mg %), are included for use by those studying isolated organs or muscles. The information is presented in a tabular form and space has been allowed for additions of new concentrations and responses of particular interest to an investigator. All non-referenced concentrations are from laboratory teaching experiments in which the temperature of the bathing or perfusing solution was kept at 37°C.

FACTORS MODIFYING DRUG RESPONSES

A search through the literature will often reveal that two investigators, studying the action of drugs under seemingly identical experimental conditions and using the same species and weight of animal, dosage, and route of administration, find quantitative and sometimes qualitative differences in drug response. Some possible sources of such variations are listed below.

Species Variation

Variation in the response of animal species to oral drug administration may be due to anatomical and/or functional differences between their digestive tracts. The carnivores (e.g., cat) possess a shorter digestive tract than herbivores (e.g., rabbit) and tend to absorb drugs more rapidly and completely. The more complex ruminant digestive system provides other variables as regards drug absorption.

The rate of metabolism of a particular drug may vary considerably in different animal species. Therefore, extreme caution should be exercised in extrapolating dosage from one species to another. For example, hexobarbital has a very short half-life in the mouse and is considered to be an ultra-short-acting anesthetic agent in this species. In the dog, on the other hand, this barbiturate shows a long half-life and is effective for hours. Another example of species variation is the response of the rabbit to atropine. The presence of an enzyme in rabbit liver, which efficiently metabolizes the drug, allows toleration of amounts of atropine that would be lethal to other species. It is evident that a "cat dose," when administered to a rabbit, would be insufficient to produce an effective cholinergic block. A safe and effective "rabbit dose" would probably prove fatal to a cat.

Individual Variation

Weight.—The weight of an animal provides an index of the amount of drug needed to raise the blood concentration to a specific level and is the most convenient factor to use in determining dosage. However, this index may prove to be misleading when considering a particular agent. For example, one could select two animals of the same weight, but with one possessing a larger amount of body fat than the other. Obviously, the same dose of a highly fat-soluble drug would not be expected to elicit the same quantitative response in the two animals.

Age.—Very young animals are more sensitive than adults to many drugs because, among other reasons, they are unable to metabolize them as rapidly and efficiently. To compensate for this difference, a generally accepted practice is to administer two-thirds of the adult dose. Old animals are frequently hypersensitive to drugs.

Sex.—Some authorities state that the female of some species is more sensitive to drugs than the male and that dosage should be modified accordingly. This is certainly true as regards the action of hexobarbital in the rat. Pregnancy or lactation may also alter drug response in the mother.

Time of Administration.—The time of administration is particularly important with respect to oral doses since most drugs are best absorbed from an "empty stomach" and for this reason they should be given after a period of fast. (Irritating drugs, however, should be administered with a meal or immediately afterwards in order to reduce their irritating effect.) The action of the central nervous system depressants is more pronounced at the end of the active day—or night if the animal is nocturnal. This may be due to fatigue and the presence of those physiological factors leading to normal sleep. Consideration should be given to the fact that some animals have a twenty-four-hour fluctuating metabolic cycle and the duration and degree of drug action may be affected by the time of administration within the diurnal cycle.

Temperament.—The individual temperament of the animal is especially important in the case of drugs acting on the central nervous system. It has been noted that a larger dose of a central nervous system depressant is needed for a hyperactive animal than for one that exhibits sluggish behavior. This generalization could be misleading, however. An apprehensive animal may develop marked constriction of splanchnic visceral blood vessels. This could result in a higher percentage of the cardiac output reaching the brain and the possibility of administering an overdose of a central nervous system depressant such as pentobarbital.

Pathology.—The presence of disease may markedly change an animal's response to drugs. Kidney damage may result in decreased drug excretion and subsequent prolonged action. Animals with impaired endocrine function may show varying sensitivity to drugs; for instance, hyperthyroidism will render an animal extremely sensitive to epinephrine, while at the same time increasing its tolerance to morphine.

Drug Variation

Physical-Chemical Properties.—Before a drug arrives at the desired site(s) of action and elicits its particular pharmacological response(s) via chemical and/or physical interaction with the tissue, it encounters various tissue "barriers" and "loss sites." The physical-chemical properties of the drug determine how much of it will ultimately reach the site of action and the magnitude and duration of the response produced. An outstanding example of a tissue "barrier" is that found between the systemic circulation and the central nervous system. The most efficient penetration of this blood-brain barrier is by a drug that shows low ionization at physiological pH and possesses a highly lipid soluble unionized moiety. An example of this type of drug is thiopental. Due to its high lipid solubility, thiopental not only enters the brain readily but has a great affinity for body fat and other tissues. These tissues then represent a "loss site" for the agent; that is, the thiopental molecules associated with tissues outside the brain are no longer available to produce central nervous system depression. Another instance of the importance of considering the chemical properties of drugs is that local or systemic changes in blood or tissue fluid pH, such as that due to impairment of respiration which results in increased pCO_2, could markedly alter the dissociation of a drug and thus either increase or decrease the amount of pharmacologically active moiety.

Secondary Drug Effects.—The pharmacological adage, "No drug has a single action," is well known but often overlooked. The transport and distribution of a particular drug depends upon the cardiovascular system. Many compounds alter cardiovascular function, resulting in changes of blood flow to various tissues. When this altered physiological state is produced as a secondary action of a drug, as for example by barbiturate anesthetics, it can complicate the interpretation of results following subsequent drug injection or other experimental procedures. The difficulties are more pronounced if one attempts to extrapolate the experimental results to the unanesthetized animal.

Drug Combinations.—Certain drugs with similar pharmacological actions, such as acid-forming salt and mercurial diuretics, when given sequentially will produce a synergistic response greater than that resulting from the sum of the responses to the separate agents. Potentiation of drug action occurs when, for example, cocaine, a compound with minimal cardiovascular activity, greatly enhances the blood pressure of subsequently injected epinephrine.

Drugs that have opposite pharmacological actions are classified as physiological antagonists. For example, pentobarbital is a central nervous system depressant, and amphetamine a stimulant. Since they probably have different sites of action in the central nervous system, the stimulatory action of amphetamine merely decreases the depressant activity of pentobarbital, and vice versa. In pharmacological antagonism, both drugs are considered to act at the same receptor site. The most dramatic example of this type of drug antagonism is seen when nalorphine is injected into an animal that is markedly depressed by morphine. The animal immediately returns to "normal." Nalorphine by itself is not a central nervous system stimulant but its antagonism results from a displacement of the morphine from its reactive site(s).

Routes of Administration

Route of administration is important in consideration of speed of onset, intensity, and duration of drug action.

ORAL ADMINISTRATION (*PO*)

The oral route of administration in animals is often used for the study of chronic drug effects or to determine factors relating to efficiency of gastrointestinal absorption. For acute experiments, this route frequently results in slow or unpredictable absorption of the drug and is seldom used except in industrial screening. In some animal species (mouse, guinea pig, rat, and rabbit), the passage of a stomach tube is relatively easy. Other species (cat, dog, and monkey) react violently to attempts at intubation.

PARENTERAL ADMINISTRATION

Intravenous (*IV*).—This route is often preferred for administering compounds in solution. Its primary advantage is that the investigator is able to slowly titrate the amount of drug needed (determined roughly by considering the animal's weight, age, sex, etc.) to elicit a particular response. Also, some drugs which are tissue irritants can be safely administered intravenously. For this technique, sharp needles and clean syringes are very important. The skin over the vein should be shaved, and, if possible, pulled taut to prevent the vein from moving. Application of small amounts of a rubefacient such as xylene will elicit total vasodilatation and facilitate injection. The skin and vein should be pierced in separate thrusts of the needle so as to avoid running the needle through the vein and producing a subsequent hematoma. A practical disadvantage of IV injection in cats, dogs, and monkeys is that usually two persons are required for the procedure.

Intraperitoneal (IP).—This method of injection is one of the most popular means of administering nonirritating chemicals. The peritoneum of the abdominal cavity presents a large absorptive area, and as long as the needle is placed in the lower quadrant and directed approximately 45° cephalad, there is little danger of piercing the abdominal viscera. This technique may usually be performed by one person, even with cats and dogs, and provides a relatively slow onset of drug effect compared to IV injection. Two problems are associated with the method. One is the "single shot" dose used; since it is not possible to titrate the drug, an overdose may be administered to a sensitive animal. Also, most of the absorbed material enters the portal circulation and there may be significant inactivation of the compound before it reaches the desired site of action. Another consideration in the use of the intraperitoneal route of administration is the volume of fluid injected. Volume is especially important with small animals such as mice, rats, and guinea pigs. The physical size of the dose can produce pressure effects which may be manifested as physiologic changes although they have nothing to do with the nature of the drug being studied. There is evidence that even the concentration of the solution used (the absolute amount of drug being the same) may considerably alter experimental results, such as those used to determine an LD_{50}.

Intramuscular (IM).—A drug may be given intramuscularly in an aqueous solution, an aqueous suspension, or in a solution or suspension in oil. The drugs are administered directly into the muscle where they spread out along the muscle fibers and fasciae. This distribution affords a large absorbing surface and results in gradual absorption. The IM route of administration is particularly useful when a prolonged effect is desired.

Subcutaneous (SC).—The subcutaneous route is used only for administering nonirritating drugs. This technique may result in a slow absorption of some drugs, especially vasoconstrictor agents. Compounds which cause local vasodilation, such as some local anesthetics, often incorporate a vasoconstrictor to slow down absorption. The site of SC injection may be quite important. For example, drugs which are administered to elicit an action on the central nervous system and are metabolized by liver enzymes, should be injected into subcutaneous areas which do not drain into the portal circulation. A common site of SC injection is the back of the neck. In this area there is usually ample loose skin which can be raised, eliminating the possibility of an intradermal injection. Aspiration of the syringe before injection will assure that the needle is not lying in a blood vessel. A modification of SC administration is pellet implantation under the skin of the back (for example, desoxycorticosterone acetate).

Intrathoracic (*IT*).—Injection of drugs high in the seventh intercostal space is a route of administration second in rapidity of onset only to the IV method; it is used extensively in veterinary medicine. There are objections to this route of administration due to the possibility of irriating lungs and pleura, but such irritation is probably insignificant in acute experiments. The amount injected should be less than that used by routes other than IV.

ANESTHESIA

The purpose of this section is to describe some of the principles, techniques, and agents that may be used to produce anesthesia in laboratory animals. There are two classes of anesthetic agents—local (or regional) and general. Agents in the first category, including compounds such as procaine, have a reversible paralytic action on nerve fibers and sensory endings. They are applied in aqueous or oily solutions to mucous or abraded surfaces; by intradermal, subdermal, or subcutaneous infiltration; and by peripheral, paravertebral, or spinal injection. Descriptions of the various local anesthetics and techniques of employing them may be found in textbooks of anesthesiology and will not be discussed here.

General anesthetic agents are divided into two categories. Those of the first, volatile or gaseous agents typified by ether and nitrous oxide, are usually administered by inhalation. Fixed anesthetics, such as pentobarbital, are examples of the second group of general anesthetics and are administered by injection. Various other compounds such as analgesics, tranquilizers, and muscle relaxants may be used as adjuncts to general anesthesia. A few examples of these agents and discussion of some of the problems associated with their use in acute experiments are presented at the end of this section.

General anesthesia refers to a physiological state, produced by agents which act on the central nervous system, characterized by loss of consciousness and voluntary motor activity. This state may be considered to be the result of a dynamic pharmacological equilibrium between the rate at which the anesthetic agent is presented to the cells of the central nervous system and the rate at which it is removed or rendered "inactive." The mechanism by which these agents produce anesthesia is the subject of much controversy. Blood concentrations of a general anesthetic required to block axonal conduction, either in peripheral nerves or in fiber tracts of the central nervous system, are approximately five times the amount necessary to elicit surgical anesthesia. Current evidence suggests that in some unknown way the anesthetics depress synaptic transmission in the reticular-cortical activating system.

The basic principles of anesthesiology are as applicable in the research laboratory as they are in the hospital operating theater, but the methods and objectives of general anesthesia in the two areas may vary considerably. This is especially true in the use of animals for acute experiments where the inclusion of a number of drugs, as part of the anesthetic regimen, could result in added variables which would be difficult to control or interpret. Many laboratory experiments utilize conscious animals following procedures, such as electrode implantation, which are performed under general anesthesia. For this purpose the important consideration is that the animal receive as many drugs as necessary to allow successful surgery and uneventful recovery. Acute experiments carried out in the anesthetized animal require a more careful choice of anesthetic agents and techniques in order to avoid adding unnecessary variables to the experiment. The following discussion provides information which may serve as a guide to the rational choice of general anesthetic agents for use in acute experiments on laboratory animals.

Many investigators will painstakingly design an acute experiment and give little or no thought to the choice of anesthetic. It appears as if they regard the anesthetic agent as producing *only* central nervous system depression, thus allowing them to work on an immobile, analgesic animal. Even a cursory glance through a pharmacology textbook will reveal the many different pharmacological actions of the various anesthetic agents and the necessity for careful consideration of these "secondary" effects in any experimental design. Another unfortunate situation is that created by investigators who use one particular general anesthetic agent, pentobarbital, for example, for all their experimental work. No one would deny that an important consideration in the use of an anesthetic is that the investigator be familiar with the actions and potential dangers of the agent. Nevertheless, the person who uses only one anesthetic for many different experimental procedures is considerably handicapping himself. The selection of a general anesthetic should be determined by the particular experimental design and animal species used, and not solely by familiarity with a particular agent.

Inhalation anesthesia allows the approximate maintenance of an equilibrium condition in the animal. These agents are "inert" in the sense of being excreted unchanged by the lungs. It is possible to establish an equilibrium between concentrations of the agent in inspired air, blood, and tissue and to maintain them within narrow limits. This permits the investigator to rapidly decrease or increase the degree of central nervous system depression. For example, if an experimental procedure requires only light anesthesia (i.e., analgesia and unconsciousness) the use of inhalation anesthetics allows one to attain reproducibly just this desired degree of depression. Using a fixed anesthetic agent such as urethane or a barbiturate, it is very difficult to maintain an animal in a constant "light" stage of anesthesia. One reason for this difficulty is that following the injection of a fixed anesthetic agent, such as a barbiturate, the animal immediately begins to inactivate the compound. Consequently, the animal is continually altering its state of drug-induced depression. It is impossible to maintain a constant blood level of the fixed anesthetics, as some investigators have tried to do by constant infusion, since the rate of biotransformation varies markedly among animals of the same species.

It is apparent from the above considerations that maintenance of reasonably constant conditions during the course of acute experiments is more feasible if one uses an inhalation agent rather than a fixed anesthetic. For example, mean arterial blood pressure progressively changes in the course of an experiment utilizing a barbiturate anesthetic. This changing base line reflects adjustments in cardiac output and/or vascular resistance. In an experiment designed to test cardiovascular reactivity of a pharmacological or physiological nature, the variability of "control" base line values makes the interpretation of results obtained quite complicated. On the other hand, due to the fine anesthetic control available when using inhalation anesthesia, it is possible to maintain a relatively constant base line and thus allow a more valid comparison of control versus experimental values.

The advantages of using inhalation anesthesia are partially offset by two serious disadvantages, namely, the requirement of constant attention by an experienced person and equipment that is usually quite expensive. A reliable and inexpensive apparatus for administering inhalation anesthetics to animals would be very useful.

No matter whether an inhalation or fixed general anesthetic is chosen, there is a good possibility that the agent will add unknown variables to the experiment. Perhaps the most outstanding example of anesthesia interfering with experimental results concerned the initial investigations of the sensory pathways between peripheral receptors and the cerebral cortex. Under anesthesia, the pathways seemed to be quite simple, but recent research has shown that while primary pathways for afferent stimuli, such as those in the thalamus, are unaffected by deep anesthesia, the secondary reticular pathways are depressed. Another example of anesthetic interference is a report by Gutman and Chainovitz (815). Small doses of pentobarbital, light anesthesia with ether or nitrous oxide, or injection of morphine converted blood pressure responses to painful stimuli in the rabbit from pressor to depressor. Chlorpromazine, an anesthetic adjunct, attenuated the reaction but did not convert it. The authors also mentioned that the same induced reversal of blood pressure response occurred when stimulating the mesencephalic reticular formation. Finally, Page and McCubbin (809) concluded from their experiments that the greatly augmented depressor activity of ganglionic blocking agents in dogs following pentobarbital anesthesia probably depends upon nearly complete inhibition of parasympathetic, cardioinhibitory activity and partial suppression of sympathetic compensatory reflexes by the action of pentobarbital. The above examples serve to demonstrate the problems which may arise from using anesthetics or anesthetic adjuncts which modify the physiological parameters under investigation.

The final part of this section provides suggestions regarding the use of general anesthesia in acute animal experiments. Seemingly insignificant or self-evident procedures are included, as these are often overlooked by an investigator:

Empty stomach.—Animals should be fasted for at least twelve hours prior to administration of the anesthetic as a safeguard against the possibility of vomiting during the experiment and the subsequent aspiration of the material into the lung.

Rapport.—"Making friends" with the animal will contribute much to a smooth anesthetic induction. Attempting to anesthetize a frightened, struggling animal, often made that way by undue restraint, may lead to fatal consequences due to the use of more anesthetic than normally required.

Route of administration.—Injectable anesthetics should be administered intravenously whenever possible. This allows titration of a maximally effective dose. Intrathoracic, subcutaneous, and intraperitoneal injections may also be utilized for administration of fixed anesthetics but possess the disadvantage that a single-dose injection may be lethal to a sensitive animal.

Temperature maintenance.—Whenever possible, the esophageal or rectal temperature of anesthetized animals should be monitored. If the temperature is known, a heating pad can be used as required to maintain a constant body temperature.

Unobstructed airway.—Placing a tracheal cannula or endotracheal tube in an anesthetized animal provides a patent airway and permits aspiration of accumulated secretions which might impair respiratory exchange.

Respiration.—Anesthetized animals tend to hypoventilate. An increase in arterial pCO_2 and subsequent pH alterations can produce major physiological changes. Arterial or end-tidal pCO_2 should be monitored so that hypoventilation can be prevented.

ANESTHETIC DOSES

The following pages present a list of fixed anesthetics and preanesthetic medications which have been successfully used in various animal species. In some instances two or more agents are listed to be used in combination. For example, atropine, morphine, and pentobarbital have been used in combination to produce anesthesia in a dog. In this case, the atropine and morphine are administered 30 and 29 minutes, respectively, prior to the pentobarbital. These two premedication agents serve to reduce the incidence of parasympathetic secretions and provide analgesia prior to administering the pentobarbital. Following the tables is a list of the major advantages and disadvantages associated with some of the more widely used anesthetic agents.

TABLE 1

Anesthetic Doses

Species	Anesthetic[a]	Page[b]	Time[c] (min.)	Route[a]	Dose (mg/kg)	Reference
Mouse	Amobarbital	33		IV	54	65
	Barbital	45		IV	234	65
	Chloral Hydrate	61		IP	400	LM[d]
	α-Chloralose	62		IP	114	204
	Chloretone (50% alcohol)			IP	175	LM
	Hexobarbital	108		IV	47	392
	Pentobarbital	168		IV	35	111
	Phenobarbital	178		IV	134	65
	Probarbital	193		IP	75	66
	Secobarbital	219		IV	30	63
	Thiopental	239		IV	25	111
	Tribromethanol	245		IV	120	66
Rat	Amobarbital	33		IV	55	63
	Barbital	45		IP	190	125
	Chloral Hydrate	61		IP	300	197
	α-Chloralose	62		IP	55	205
	Diallybarbituric Acid	78		SC	60	66
	Hexobarbital	108		IP	75	393
	Pentobarbital	168		IV	25	111
	Phenobarbital	178		IV	100	589
	Probarbital	193		SC	225	66
	Secobarbital	219		IV	17.5	63
	Thiopental	239		IV	25	111
	Tribromethanol	245		IP	550	547
	Urethane	251		IP	780	127
Guinea Pig	Amobarbital	33		IV	50	63
	Chloretone (in 50% alcohol)			IP	175	LM
	Pentobarbital	168		IV	30	111
	Phenobarbital	178		IP	100	LM
	Secobarbital	219		IV	20	63
	Thiopental	239		IV	20	111
	Tribromethanol	245		IV	100	66
	Urethane	251		IP	1500	LM
Rabbit	Amobarbital	33		IV	40	72
	Barbital	45		IV	175	LM
	α-Chloralose	62		IV	120	LM
	Morphine	154	30	SC	10	LM
	Chloretone (in 50% alcohol)			PO	175	LM

[a]Other routes of administration may be found in the main body of the handbook.

[b]The page numbers refer to the main body of the handbook where additional dosage information may be obtained.

[c]The numbers refer to time elapsed (in minutes) before the injection of the following drug.

[d]LM means that the dose was obtained from a pharmacology teaching manual.

TABLE 1 (continued)

Species	Anesthetic	Page	Time (min.)	Route	Dose (mg/kg)	Reference
Rabbit (cont'd)	Diallylbarbituric Acid	78		IV	50	LM
	Hexobarbital	108		IV	25	LM
	Paraldehyde	165		IV	300	7
	Pentobarbital	168		IV	30	111
	Phenobarbital	178		IV	200	590
	Probarbital	193		IP	66	66
	Secobarbital	219		IV	22.5	72
	Thiopental	239		IV	20	111
	Tribromethanol	245		IV	80	66
	Urethane	251		IV	1000	LM
	Urethane	251		IP	700 }	305
	Pentobarbital	168		IP	40 }	
Cat	Amobarbital	33		IV	11	24
	Barbital	45		IV	200	LM
	Chloral Hydrate	61		PO	250	LM
	α-Chloralose	62		IV	75	208
	α-Chloralose	62		IV	50 }	747
	Urethane	251		IV	50 }	
	α-Chloralose	62		IV	80 }	748
	Pentobarbital	168		IV	12 }	
	α-Chloralose	62		IV	80 }	154
	Pentobarbital	168		IV	6 }	
	Diallylbarbituric Acid	78		IV	36	291
	Hexobarbital	108		IV	25	66
	Paraldehyde	165		IV	300	7
	Pentobarbital	168		IV	25	111
	Phenobarbital	178		IP	180	LM
	Secobarbital	219		IV	25	63
	Thiopental	239		IV	28	24
	Tribromethanol	245		IV	100	557
	Urethane	251		IV	1250	LM
	Urethane	251		IP	400 }	749
	α-Chloralose	62		IP	50 }	
	Urethane	251		IP	280 }	750
	Diallylbarbituric Acid	78		IP	70 }	
	Urethane	251		IP	360 }	408
	Diallylbarbituric Acid	78		IP	90 }	
	Urethane	251		IP	250 }	LM
	Pentobarbital	168		IP	30 }	
Dog	Amobarbital	33		IV	50	LM
	Barbital	45		IV	220	LM
	Barbital	45		IV	250 }	LM
	Thiopental	239		IV	15 }	
	Barbital	45		IV	220 }	422
	Pentobarbital	168		IV	15 }	

TABLE 1 (continued)

Species	Anesthetic	Page	Time (min.)	Route	Dose (mg/kg)	Reference
Dog (cont'd)	Chloral Hydrate	61		IV	125	LM
	α-Chloralose	62		IV	100	209
	Morphine	154	30	SC	1	490
	α-Chloralose	62		IV	100	
	Morphine	154	60	SC	1	753
	α-Chloralose	62		IV	80	
	α-Chloralose	62		IV	50	LM
	Thiopental	239		IV	15	
	Morphine	154	30	SC	10	LM
	Chloretone (in 50% alcohol)			PO	225	
	Hexobarbital	108		IV	30	66
	Paraldehyde	165		IV	300	7
	Pentobarbital	168		IP	30	497
	Drip—6 mg/kg/min.			IV		
	Morphine	154	30	SC	10	751
	Pentobarbital	168		IV	20	
	Morphine	154	30	IM	2	747
	Pentobarbital	168		IV	15	
	Morphine	154	60	IM	3	458
	Pentobarbital	168		IV	12	
	Atropine	41	30	SC	1	LM
	Morphine	154	30	SC	10	
	Pentobarbital	168		IV	30	
	Phenobarbital	178		IV	80	591
	Phenobarbital	178		IV	200	LM
	Thiopental	239		IV	15	
	Secobarbital	219		PO	40	63
	Thiopental	239		IV	25	716
	Tribromethanol	245		IV	125	557
	Urethane	251		IV	1000	413
	Urethane	251		IV	480	752
	α-Chloralose	62		IV	48	
	Morphine	154		IV	2	
	Morphine	154	60	SC	2	742
	Urethane	251		IV	250	
	α-Chloralose	62		IV	60	
	Morphine	154	60	SC	3	LM
	Urethane	251		IV	50	
	α-Chloralose	62		IV	13	
	Diallylbarbituric Acid	78		IV	8	
	Morphine	154	30	SC	5	LM
	Urethane	251		PO	1500	

TABLE 1 (continued)

Species	Anesthetic	Page	Time (min.)	Route	Dose (mg/kg)	Reference
Monkey	Amobarbital	33		IV	40	63
	Pentobarbital	168		IV	25	111
	Phenobarbital	178		IP	100	161
	Secobarbital	219		IV	17.5	63

TABLE 2

Advantages and Disadvantages of Anesthetic Agents and Adjuncts

Agent	Advantages	Disadvantages
1. Anesthetics		
α-Chloralose	Less reflex depression than barbiturates. Blood pressure and respiration stable for 3-4 hours.	Low water solubility. Can make up 10% solution in polyethylene glycol 200.
Pentobarbital	Fairly long duration. Readily available in solution.	Tachycardia, depression of cardiovascular and spinal cord reflexes.
Thiopental	Short duration (15-30 min.) useful to induce anesthesia before using inhalation agents.	Irritating to tissues. Solution rapidly decomposes. Marked respiratory depression.
Urethane	Little reflex depression. Readily soluble in water. Duration of 3-4 hours.	Because of liver and bone marrow toxicity, only used in acute experiments.
Dial (Ciba)*	More rapid onset than urethane alone. Less reflex depression than with barbiturate alone and less toxicity than with urethane alone.	Only for acute experiments.
2. Adjuncts to Anesthesia		
Atropine	Decreases tracheal secretions; hence useful as preanesthetic medication for inhalation anesthesia.	Suppresses vagal tone to heart. May elicit ganglionic blockade in "high" doses.
Chlorpromazine	Produces sedation and thereby reduces the amount of anesthetic needed.	Has many pharmacological actions. Advise against its use in acute experiments as preanesthetic medication.
Curare	Allows muscle relaxation at light stage of anesthesia.	Possibility of histamine release. Danger of respiratory paralysis.
Morphine	Produces analgesia and sedation, thus facilitating anesthesia.	Respiratory depressant. Has other poorly defined actions on CNS and autonomic nervous system.

*Contains: Urethane, 400 mg/ml.
Diallylbarbituric Acid, 100 mg/ml.

DRUG DOSAGE TABLES

Note: Ten blank pages have been provided in the back of this volume, permitting addition in alphabetical order of further drug data which may be accumulated by the user of the handbook. The authors would be grateful if users submitted such further data and/or comments and suggestions regarding the handbook to them, in care of the University of California Press, Berkeley, California 94720, so that the new information can be included in later editions.

ACETALDEHYDE

(Ethanal, Acetic Aldehyde, Ethylaldehyde)

mg/kg		Mouse	Rat	Guinea Pig	Rabbit	Cat	Dog	Monkey	
Lethal Dose Y–LD_{50} Z–MLD	IV				Y300 [3]	300 [4]			
	IP		500 [2]						
	IM								
	SC	Y560 [1]	Y640 [1]		Y1200 [3]				
	PO		Y1900						
Hypnotic	IV						8.5 [4]		
	IP				700 [4]				
	IM				700 [4]				
	SC				700 [4]				
	PO								
Sympatho-mimetic	IV					10 [5]	10		
	IP								
	IM								
	SC								
	PO								
	IV								
	IP								
	IM								
	SC								
	PO								

IN VITRO

mg %	Cardiac	Vascular	Gut	Uterine	Visceral	Skeletal		

ACETANILIDE

(N-phenylacetamide, Antifebrin, Acetylaniline)

mg/kg		Mouse	Rat	Guinea Pig	Rabbit	Cat	Dog	Monkey	
Lethal Dose Y−LD_{50} Z−MLD	IV					13.5 [11]	300 [11]	300 [7]	
	IP		Y800						
	IM								
	SC	1300 [6]							
	PO	1840 [7]	Y800 [8]	1500 [7]	1500 [11]	250 [11]	700 [12]		
Toxic Dose	IV						62 [7]	275 [7]	
	IP								
	IM								
	SC	1200 [7]							
	PO	1840 [7]	500 [10]		1200 [7]		700 [7]	600 [7]	
Analgetic Antipyretic	IV								
	IP		400 [9]						
	IM								
	SC								
	PO					*125	*500		
	IV								
	IP								
	IM								
	SC								
	PO								

*Total dose

IN VITRO

mg %	Cardiac	Vascular	Gut	Uterine	Visceral	Skeletal		

ACETYLCHOLINE

(Acecoline, Arterocoline, Ovisot)

mg/kg		Mouse	Rat	Guinea Pig	Rabbit	Cat	Dog	Monkey	
Lethal Dose Y–LD_{50} Z–MLD	IV	Y20 13	Y22 13		Y0.3				
	IP								
	IM								
	SC	Y170 13	Y250			Y10 15			
	PO	Y3000 13	Y2500 13						
Parasympatho-mimetic	IV		0.01		0.01	0.01	0.01		
	IP								
	IM								
	SC				1.0 14				
	PO				1,000 14				
Nicotinic (Atropinized Animal)	IV				0.1	0.1	0.1		
	IP								
	IM								
	SC								
	PO								
	IV								
	IP								
	IM								
	SC								
	PO								

IN VITRO

mg %	Cardiac	Vascular	Gut	Uterine	Visceral	Skeletal		
Guinea Pig	0.025		0.01	0.02	0.02 16			
Rabbit	0.003 16		0.02 16	0.05 16	0.07 16			
Dog			0.003 16	0.1 16	0.03 16			

ACETYLSALICYLIC ACID

(Aspirin, Acetophen, Acesal)

mg/kg		Mouse	Rat	Guinea Pig	Rabbit	Cat	Dog	Monkey	
Lethal Dose Y–LD_{50} Z–MLD	IV				Z700 4				
	IP	Y495 17	Y500 19						
	IM								
	SC				Z700 23				
	PO	Y1100 18	Y1500 20		Y1800 18		Y3000		
Analgetic Antipyretic	IV								
	IP			269 22					
	IM								
	SC	400							
	PO		450 21		*500 4	*200 24	*200 24	100 25	
Toxic Dose (Convulsant)	IV								
	IP								
	IM								
	SC								
	PO	700 7					750 4		
Block Bradykinin Bronchio-constriction	IV			2 26					
	IP								
	IM								
	SC								
	PO								
	IV								
	IP								
	IM								
	SC								
	PO								
	IV								
	IP								
	IM								
	SC								
	PO								

*Total dose

ALCOHOL, ANHYDROUS

(Ethanol, Ethyl Alcohol)

mg/kg		Mouse	Rat	Guinea Pig	Rabbit	Cat	Dog	Monkey	
Lethal Dose Y–LD_{50} Z–MLD	IV	Y1953 [27]				3945 [33]	5365 [35]		
	IP		Y5000 [29]	Y5560 [4]					
	IM								
	SC	Y8285 [27]					7000		
	PO	Y9488 [27]	Y13,660 [4]		Y9500 [29]		6000		
Increase Brain Serotonin	IV								
	IP		4475 [31]						
	IM								
	SC								
	PO								
Behavioral	IV								
	IP		15 [32]						
	IM								
	SC								
	PO								
CNS	IV					4.6 [34]			
	IP								
	IM								
	SC								
	PO								
Paralytic	IV								
	IP	4000 [28]		4000 [4]		4000 [4]			
	IM								
	SC								
	PO			4000 [4]	5000 [4]	4000 [4]			
	IV								
	IP								
	IM								
	SC								
	PO								

ALLOXAN

(Mesoxalylurea, Mesoxalylcarbamide)

mg/kg		Mouse	Rat	Guinea Pig	Rabbit	Cat	Dog	Monkey	
Lethal Dose Y–LD_{50} Z–MLD	IV	Y200 [36]	300 [37]		200 [7]		100 [41]		
	IP	Y350 [36]							
	IM								
	SC								
	PO								
Diabetogenic	IV		40 [38]						
	IP		200 [39]						
	IM								
	SC		200 [40]						
	PO					750 [7]			
	IV								
	IP								
	IM								
	SC								
	PO								
	IV								
	IP								
	IM								
	SC								
	PO								
	IV								
	IP								
	IM								
	SC								
	PO								
	IV								
	IP								
	IM								
	SC								
	PO								

ALPHAPRODINE

(Nisentil, Nu 1196, Prisilidene)

mg/kg		Mouse	Rat	Guinea Pig	Rabbit	Cat	Dog	Monkey	
Lethal Dose $Y-LD_{50}$ $Z-MLD$	IV	Y54 [42]		Y18 [42]	Y18.5				
	IP	Y73 [42]	Y22 [42]						
	IM								
	SC	Y98 [42]	Y23 [42]						
	PO		Y90 [43]						
Analgetic	IV								
	IP								
	IM								
	SC		3 [43]				20		
	PO		10 [43]						
Cardiovascular and Respiratory	IV				1.5 [43]		1.0 [42]		
	IP								
	IM								
	SC								
	PO								
Increase Intestinal Tone	IV						1.0 [43]		
	IP								
	IM								
	SC								
	PO								
	IV								
	IP								
	IM								
	SC								
	PO								
	IV								
	IP								
	IM								
	SC								
	PO								

AMIDOPYRINE

(Dipirin, Aminopyrine, Pyramidon)

mg/kg		Mouse	Rat	Guinea Pig	Rabbit	Cat	Dog	Monkey	
Lethal Dose Y–LD_{50} Z–MLD	IV	Y184 49	Z135 51						
	IP		Y248 52						
	IM								
	SC	Y350 49			417 56		300 57		
	PO	Y1850 49	Y1700	Z925 4	Z750 4				
Analgetic Antipyretic Anti-inflammatory	IV				50 50				
	IP	150 50							
	IM								
	SC		200 50						
	PO	300 7	650 50	130 55			*265 24		
Hypothermic	IV								
	IP				100 4				
	IM				100 4				
	SC		150 54		100 4				
	PO								
	IV								
	IP								
	IM								
	SC								
	PO								

*Total dose

IN VITRO

mg %	Cardiac	Vascular	Gut	Uterine	Visceral	Skeletal		

AMINOPHYLLINE

(Theophylline ethylenediamine, Carena, Inophylline)

mg/kg		Mouse	Rat	Guinea Pig	Rabbit	Cat	Dog	Monkey	
Lethal Dose Y–LD50 Z–MLD	IV		Z190 [77]		Y150 [45]				
	IP								
	IM								
	SC	Z140 [7]							
	PO	Y540							
Cardiovascular	IV		150 [44]		35 [46]	35 [46]	10		
	IP								
	IM								
	SC								
	PO		100 [44]						
Diuretic	IV						20		
	IP								
	IM								
	SC								
	PO		20 [44]						
	IV								
	IP								
	IM								
	SC								
	PO								

IN VITRO

mg %	Cardiac	Vascular	Gut	Uterine	Visceral	Skeletal		
Langendorff (Perfusion)	*5							

*Total mg

α-(l-AMINOPROPYL) PROTOCATECHUYL ALCOHOL

(Ethylnorepinephrine, Butanephrine, Bronkephrine)

mg/kg		Mouse	Rat	Guinea Pig	Rabbit	Cat	Dog	Monkey	
Lethal Dose Y–LD_{50} Z–MLD	IV	Y117 [47]							
	IP								
	IM								
	SC								
	PO								
Bronchiolar Dilatation	IV					1 [48]	1 [47]		
	IP			500 [47]					
	IM								
	SC		80 [47]						
	PO								
Hyperglycemic	IV								
	IP								
	IM								
	SC				10 [47]				
	PO								
	IV								
	IP								
	IM								
	SC								
	PO								

IN VITRO

mg %	Cardiac	Vascular	Gut	Uterine	Visceral	Skeletal		

AMITRIPTYLINE

(Elavil)

mg/kg		Mouse	Rat	Guinea Pig	Rabbit	Cat	Dog	Monkey	
Lethal Dose Y–LD_{50} Z–MLD	IV	Y27 [58]			Y9.9 [58]				
	IP	Y76 [58]	Y72 [58]						
	IM								
	SC	Y328 [58]	Y1290 [58]						
	PO	Y289 [58]	Y530 [58]						
Analeptic to Tetrabenazine	IV								
	IP	1.0 [58]	20 [59]						
	IM								
	SC								
	PO	1.0 [58]							
Adrenolytic	IV						1.2 [58]		
Hypothermic	IP	30 [59]	30 [59]						
	IM								
	SC								
	PO								
Behavioral	IV								
	IP		40 [59]						
	IM								
	SC								
	PO								
	IV								
	IP								
	IM								
	SC								
	PO								
	IV								
	IP								
	IM								
	SC								
	PO								

AMMONIUM CHLORIDE

(Ammonium Muriate, Sal Ammoniac, Salmiac)

mg/kg		Mouse	Rat	Guinea Pig	Rabbit	Cat	Dog	Monkey	
Lethal Dose Y–LD_{50} Z–MLD	IV			240 [62]					
	IP								
	IM								
	SC	500							
	PO								
Diuretic	IV								
	IP		250 [61]						
	IM								
	SC								
	PO		250						
Medullary Stimulant	IV	150 [4]	150 [4]	150 [4]	150 [4]	150 [4]	150 [4]	150 [4]	
	IP								
	IM								
	SC								
	PO								
	IV								
	IP								
	IM								
	SC								
	PO								

IN VITRO

mg %	Cardiac	Vascular	Gut	Uterine	Visceral	Skeletal		

AMOBARBITAL

(Amytal, Dorminal, Amytalily)

mg/kg		Mouse	Rat	Guinea Pig	Rabbit	Cat	Dog	Monkey	
Lethal Dose Y–LD_{50} Z–MLD	IV	Z135 [63]	Z90 [63]	Z80 [63]	Y75 [70]	54	61 [64]		
	IP	200 [64]	Y115	Z120 [63]	90 [66]	Z120 [63]			
	IM		Z230 [4]						
	SC	Z280 [63]	190 [68]	Z170 [63]	Z150 [63]				
	PO		400 [63]		Y575 [71]	Y110	125 [63]		
Anesthetic	IV	54 [65]	55 [63]	50 [63]	40 [72]	11 [24]	50	40 [63]	
	IP	65 [66]	100 [4]	60 [63]	54 [66]	75	65		
	IM				50	100 [4]			
	SC	130 [63]	150	85 [63]	70 [66]	100 [4]	105		
	PO		225 [69]		90 [66]	100	175 [66]		
Spinal Cord Depressant	IV					30			
	IP								
	IM								
	SC								
	PO								
	IV								
	IP								
	IM								
	SC								
	PO								
	IV								
	IP								
	IM								
	SC								
	PO								
	IV								
	IP								
	IM								
	SC								
	PO								

AMPHETAMINE

(Benzedrine, Alentol, Ortedrine)

mg/kg		Mouse	Rat	Guinea Pig	Rabbit	Cat	Dog	Monkey	
Lethal Dose $Y-LD_{50}$ Z−MLD	IV	Y25 [73]			25 [52]				
	IP	Y120 [74]	Y125 [80]						
	IM								
	SC	270 [75]	Y160 [81]						
	PO	22 [73]	Y60.5 [82]		Y85		Z20 [83]		
Sympatho-mimetic	IV			0.5	0.5	0.5	0.5		
	IP		10 [7]						
	IM								
	SC		80 [83]						
	PO								
CNS Stimulant	IV				0.75 [87]	1.5	2.5		
	IP								
	IM								
	SC	5 [76]	3 [84]			1.5 [24]			
	PO		2						
Antagonize Reserpine Ptosis	IV								
	IP	2.5 [78]							
	IM								
	SC								
	PO	4 [79]							
Increase Spontaneous Motor Activity	IV								
	IP								
	IM								
	SC		0.68 [85]					5 [89]	
	PO								
Behavioral	IV								
	IP								
	IM							*1.15 [90]	
	SC								
	PO								

*Total dose

mg/kg		Mouse	Rat	Guinea Pig	Rabbit	Cat	Dog	Monkey	
Decrease Tissue Uptake of Norepinephrine	IV					10 [91]			
	IP								
	IM								
	SC								
	PO								
Increase Digestion Time	IV								
	IP		10 [7]						
	IM								
	SC								
	PO								
	IV								
	IP								
	IM								
	SC								
	PO								
	IV								
	IP								
	IM								
	SC								
	PO								

IN VITRO

mg %	Cardiac	Vascular	Gut	Uterine	Visceral	Skeletal		
Antiserotonergic			10 [92]					

ANGIOTONIN

(Hypertensin, Angiotensin)

mg/kg		Mouse	Rat	Guinea Pig	Rabbit	Cat	Dog	Monkey	
Lethal Dose Y–LD_{50} Z–MLD	IV		8 [93]						
	IP								
	IM								
	SC								
	PO								
Cardiovascular	IV		0.0002 [93]			0.0001 [93]	0.0001 [93]		
	IP								
	IM								
	SC					0.0005 [93]			
	PO								
	IV								
	IP								
	IM								
	SC								
	PO								
	IV								
	IP								
	IM								
	SC								
	PO								

IN VITRO

mg %	Cardiac	Vascular	Gut	Uterine	Visceral	Skeletal		
Contractile		0.001 [93]	0.001 [93]					

ANILERIDINE

(Leritine, MK89)

mg/kg		Mouse	Rat	Guinea Pig	Rabbit	Cat	Dog	Monkey	
Lethal Dose Y–LD_{50} Z–MLD	IV	*Y25 58							
	IP	*Y53 58	*Y45 58						
	IM								
	SC	*Y100 58	*Y163 58						
	PO	*Y128 58	*Y175 58						
Analgetic	IV								
	IP								
	IM							*1.25 58	
	SC		*5 58				*5 58		
	PO		*12 58				*5 58		
Cardiovascular	IV					2 94	2 94		
	IP								
	IM								
	SC								
	PO								
Respiratory Depression	IV					4 94	4 94		
	IP								
	IM								
	SC								
	PO								
	IV								
	IP								
	IM								
	SC								
	PO								
	IV								
	IP								
	IM								
	SC								
	PO								

* as base

APOMORPHINE

mg/kg		Mouse	Rat	Guinea Pig	Rabbit	Cat	Dog	Monkey	
Lethal Dose Y–LD_{50} Z–MLD	IV		40 [95]				Y80		
	IP								
	IM								
	SC								
	PO								
Emetic	IV					30 [96]	0.075		
	IP								
	IM								
	SC					30 [96]	0.1		
	PO						200 [4]		
Morphine Antagonist	IV								
	IP								
	IM								
	SC						1		
	PO								
CNS Stimulant	IV		10 [95]						
	IP								
	IM								
	SC								
	PO								
	IV								
	IP								
	IM								
	SC								
	PO								
	IV								
	IP								
	IM								
	SC								
	PO								

ARTERENOL

(Aktamin, Levophed, Norepinephrine)

mg/kg		Mouse	Rat	Guinea Pig	Rabbit	Cat	Dog	Monkey	
Lethal Dose Y–LD_{50} Z–MLD	IV								
	IP								
	IM								
	SC								
	PO								
Cardiovascular	IV	0.003 [97]	0.003 [97]	0.003 [97]	0.003 [97]	0.003 [97]	0.003 [97]		
	IP								
	IM								
	SC								
	PO								
Behavioral	IV						0.01 [90]		
	IP								
	IM								
	SC								
	PO								
Barbiturate Sleep Potentiation	IV								
	IP	2 [98]							
	IM								
	SC								
	PO								
Antagonize Reserpine Ptosis	IV								
	IP	1 [78]							
	IM								
	SC								
	PO								
Diuretic	IV								
	IP								
	IM								
	SC		0.25 [151]						
	PO								

mg/kg		Mouse	Rat	Guinea Pig	Rabbit	Cat	Dog	Monkey	
	IV								
	IP								
	IM								
	SC								
	PO								
	IV								
	IP								
	IM								
	SC								
	PO								
	IV								
	IP								
	IM								
	SC								
	PO								
	IV								
	IP								
	IM								
	SC								
	PO								

IN VITRO

mg %	Cardiac	Vascular	Gut	Uterine	Visceral	Skeletal		
Langendorff	*0.1							
Antiserotonergic			0.008 92					

*Total mg

ATROPINE

(Atropisol)

mg/kg		Mouse	Rat	Guinea Pig	Rabbit	Cat	Dog	Monkey	
Lethal Dose Y–LD_{50} Z–MLD	IV	Y90 [100]			71 [107]	Z30 [109]	100 [104]		
	IP	Y250 [101]	Y280 [101]	Y400 [101]			175 [104]		
	IM								
	SC	Y900 [101]	750 [101]	450 [104]	375 [107]	140 [104]	225 [104]		
	PO	Y400 [102]	Y750 [101]	Y1100 [101]	1450 [107]				
Anticholinergic	IV				2	2 [109]	1		
	IP		0.5 [103]						
	IM			5	0.11 [101]				
	SC	0.05 [101]	3 [101]			0.6 [110]	0.5		
	PO	0.55 [101]	10 [101]						
Preanesthetic Medication	IV								
	IP								
	IM					1.0 [557]	2.75 [557]		
	SC	0.05 [97]	0.05 [97]	0.05 [97]	0.05 [97]	0.05 [557]	0.1	0.05 [97]	
	PO			1 [105]					
CNS	IV				3 [108]	4 [112]			
	IP					4 [112]			
	IM								
	SC								
	PO								
Behavioral	IV								
	IP		15 [106]						
	IM								
	SC								
	PO								
Antiseroton-ergic	IV			10 [92]					
	IP								
	IM								
	SC								
	PO								

ATROPINE (continued)

mg/kg		Mouse	Rat	Guinea Pig	Rabbit	Cat	Dog	Monkey	
Protect Against Coronary Occlusion	IV						0.1 [7]		
	IP								
	IM								
	SC								
	PO								
Block Superior Cervical Ganglion Transmission	IV					2.5 [113]			
	IP								
	IM								
	SC								
	PO								
	IV								
	IP								
	IM								
	SC								
	PO								
	IV								
	IP								
	IM								
	SC								
	PO								

IN VITRO

mg %	Cardiac	Vascular	Gut	Uterine	Visceral	Skeletal		
Anticholinergic	0.1		0.01 [101]	0.1	0.01			
Antiserotonergic Rat			1.0 [92]					
Antiserotonergic G.P.			0.5 [92]					

ATROPINE METHYL NITRATE

(Eumydrin, Harvatrate, Metropine)

mg/kg		Mouse	Rat	Guinea Pig	Rabbit	Cat	Dog	Monkey	
Lethal Dose Y–LD_{50} Z–MLD	IV								
	IP	Y250							
	IM								
	SC								
	PO								
Cardiovascular	IV			2		1.5	3		
	IP								
	IM								
	SC								
	PO								
CNS	IV					10 [114]			
	IP								
	IM								
	SC								
	PO								
	IV								
	IP								
	IM								
	SC								
	PO								

IN VITRO

mg %	Cardiac	Vascular	Gut	Uterine	Visceral	Skeletal		
Anticholinergic	10		10					

AZACYCLONOL

(Frenquel, MER-17, Gamma-Pipradol)

mg/kg		Mouse	Rat	Guinea Pig	Rabbit	Cat	Dog	Monkey	
Lethal Dose Y–LD_{50} Z–MLD	IV	Y177 [115]					45 [117]		
	IP	Y220 [115]							
	IM								
	SC	Y350 [115]							
	PO	Y650 [115]							
Decreased Spontaneous Motor Activity	IV	93 [116]							
	IP								
	IM								
	SC	213 [116]							
	PO	520 [116]							
Hexobarbital Sleep Potentiation	IV								
	IP	78 [117]							
	IM								
	SC	71 [116]							
	PO	100 [118]							
Cardiovascular	IV						32 [117]		
	IP								
	IM								
	SC								
	PO	300 [119]							
Hypothermic	IV								
	IP								
	IM				10 [120]				
	SC								
	PO								
	IV								
	IP								
	IM								
	SC								
	PO								

BARBITAL

(Veronal, Medinal, Barbitone)

mg/kg		Mouse	Rat	Guinea Pig	Rabbit	Cat	Dog	Monkey	
Lethal Dose Y–LD_{50} Z–MLD	IV	440 [27]			350 [66]				
	IP	Y760 [122]	300 [66]		375 [128]				
	IM								
	SC	340 [66]	330 [66]		350 [66]	300			
	PO	600	400		Z275 [129]	275 [66]	350 [66]		
Anesthetic	IV	234 [65]			175	200	220		
	IP	300 [124]	190 [125]				250		
	IM								
	SC		200 [126]		110 [66]				
	PO		190 [125]		110 [66]	150 [66]			
Hypnotic	IV				130				
	IP		145 [127]						
	IM								
	SC								
	PO					*200 [24]	*550 [24]		
Behavioral	IV						125		
	IP								
	IM								
	SC								
	PO						2000 [30]		
	IV								
	IP								
	IM								
	SC								
	PO								
	IV								
	IP								
	IM								
	SC								
	PO								

*Total dose

BARIUM CHLORIDE

mg/kg		Mouse	Rat	Guinea Pig	Rabbit	Cat	Dog	Monkey	
Lethal Dose Y–LD_{50} Z–MLD	IV		Z20 [53]		17 [86]	50 [86]	26 [86]		
	IP	Y500							
	IM								
	SC		Y178 [82]	55 [86]	55 [82]	38 [82]	15 [86]		
	PO		335 [82]		170 [82]		90		
Cardiovascular	IV			10			7.5		
	IP								
	IM								
	SC		35 [82]						
	PO								
	IV								
	IP								
	IM								
	SC								
	PO								
	IV								
	IP								
	IM								
	SC								
	PO								

IN VITRO

mg %	Cardiac	Vascular	Gut	Uterine	Visceral	Skeletal		
Spasmogenic	5	2	3 [88]		10			

BEMEGRIDE

(Megimide, Mikedimide, Eukraton)

mg/kg		Mouse	Rat	Guinea Pig	Rabbit	Cat	Dog	Monkey	
Lethal Dose Y–LD_{50} Z–MLD	IV	Y20 [111]	Y16.3 [121]	Y26.5 [131]	Y25 [121]				
	IP	Y45 [111]	Y23.5 [121]						
	IM								
	SC	Y43 [121]							
	PO	Y100 [111]							
Analeptic	IV	10 [111]		10 [131]	1.0 [132]	14 [97]	10 [133]		
	IP		30 [123]			14 [97]	20 [97]		
	IM								
	SC								
	PO								
Convulsant	IV	20.1 [121]	9.5 [121]	18.5 [131]	5.5 [121]	4.5 [134]			
	IP		20 [130]						
	IM								
	SC	43 [121]							
	PO								
	IV								
	IP								
	IM								
	SC								
	PO								

IN VITRO

mg %	Cardiac	Vascular	Gut	Uterine	Visceral	Skeletal		

BENACTYZINE

(Suavitil, Parasan, Cafron)

mg/kg		Mouse	Rat	Guinea Pig	Rabbit	Cat	Dog	Monkey	
Lethal Dose Y–LD_{50} Z–MLD	IV				15 [135]				
	IP	115 [135]	115 [135]	115 [135]	115 [135]				
	IM								
	SC	Y250 [136]							
	PO	Y350 [119]							
Behavioral	IV				1 [132]	4.7 [145]			
	IP	22 [137]	50 [106]						
	IM								
	SC	50 [138]	20 [143]			6 [135]			
	PO								
Barbiturate Sleep Potentiation	IV				5 [141]				
	IP	5 [141]							
	IM								
	SC	5 [142]		30 [142]	25 [142]				
	PO			50 [142]					
Anticonvulsant	IV				1 [132]				
	IP	10 [139]		15 [132]					
	IM	2 [140]							
	SC								
	PO								
Anticholinergic	IV				0.5 [135]	0.1 [135]			
	IP		24 [144]						
	IM								
	SC								
	PO								
	IV								
	IP								
	IM								
	SC								
	PO								

BENZATROPINE

(Cogentin, Amilyt, Cobretin)

mg/kg		Mouse	Rat	Guinea Pig	Rabbit	Cat	Dog	Monkey	
Lethal Dose Y–LD_{50} Z–MLD (base)	IV	Y25 [58]							
	IP								
	IM								
	SC	Y103 [58]	Y353 [58]						
	PO	Y94 [58]							
Anticholinergic (base)	IV					1 [58]			
	IP								
	IM								
	SC								
	PO								
Antagonize Tremorine (base)	IV								
	IP	1.5 [58]							
	IM								
	SC								
	PO								
	IV								
	IP								
	IM								
	SC								
	PO								

IN VITRO

mg %	Cardiac	Vascular	Gut	Uterine	Visceral	Skeletal		

BISHYDROXYCUMARIN

(Dicumarol, Dicourmarin, Melitoxin)

mg/kg		Mouse	Rat	Guinea Pig	Rabbit	Cat	Dog	Monkey	
Lethal Dose Y-LD_{50} Z-MLD	IV	Y64 146	Y52 146	Y59 146			40		
	IP	Y350							
	IM								
	SC								
	PO	Y233 146	Y542 146						
Anticoagulant	IV						10 7		
	IP								
	IM								
	SC								
	PO		8 147				20		
	IV								
	IP								
	IM								
	SC								
	PO								
	IV								
	IP								
	IM								
	SC								
	PO								

IN VITRO

mg %	Cardiac	Vascular	Gut	Uterine	Visceral	Skeletal		

BRETYLIUM

(Darenthin)

mg/kg		Mouse	Rat	Guinea Pig	Rabbit	Cat	Dog	Monkey	
Lethal Dose Y–LD_{50} Z–MLD	IV	Y20 [148]							
	IP	Y49 [149]							
	IM								
	SC	Y72 [148]							
	PO	Y400 [148]						>400 [149]	
Sympatholytic	IV	12.5 [148]	5 [150]			15 [153]	5 [154]		
	IP								
	IM								
	SC								
	PO		400 [148]					200 [148]	
Neuromuscular Block	IV								
	IP								
	IM								
	SC					100 [148]		50 [148]	
	PO								
Increased Norepinephrine in Liver, Heart and Kidney	IV								
	IP			50 [152]					
	IM								
	SC								
	PO								
Diuretic	IV								
	IP								
	IM								
	SC		100 [151]						
	PO								
Prevent Guanethidine Depletion of Heart Catechol Amines	IV		5 [150]						
	IP								
	IM								
	SC								
	PO								

BRETYLIUM (continued)

mg/kg		Mouse	Rat	Guinea Pig	Rabbit	Cat	Dog	Monkey	
	IV								
	IP								
	IM								
	SC								
	PO								
	IV								
	IP								
	IM								
	SC								
	PO								
	IV								
	IP								
	IM								
	SC								
	PO								
	IV								
	IP								
	IM								
	SC								
	PO								

IN VITRO

mg %	Cardiac	Vascular	Gut	Uterine	Visceral	Skeletal		
Finkleman [812]			0.3 [148]					
Rabbit Ear		0.1 [148]						
Guinea Pig	0.5		20 [148]	15 [148]				
Rat Diaphragm						40 [148]		

BUFOTENINE

(Mapine, N-N-dimethylserotonin)

mg/kg		Mouse	Rat	Guinea Pig	Rabbit	Cat	Dog	Monkey	
Lethal Dose Y–LD_{50} Z–MLD	IV								
	IP		125 [155]						
	IM								
	SC								
	PO								
Behavioral	IV				1 [157]		1 [160]	10 [161]	
	IP	5 [156]	5 [156]						
	IM							10 [161]	
	SC		5 [156]						
	PO								
Cardiovascular	IV				0.1 [158]	0.1 [158]	0.05 [158]		
	IP		0.1 [155]						
	IM								
	SC								
	PO								
EEG (synchronization)	IV				0.08 [159]				
	IP								
	IM								
	SC				2.5 [156]				
	PO								
	IV								
	IP								
	IM								
	SC								
	PO								
	IV								
	IP								
	IM								
	SC								
	PO								

BULBOCAPNINE

mg/kg		Mouse	Rat	Guinea Pig	Rabbit	Cat	Dog	Monkey	
Lethal Dose Y–LD50 Z–MLD	IV								
	IP								
	IM								
	SC	Y195 [162]							
	PO								
Catatonic	IV						40 [169]		
	IP	125 [163]	50 [165]					10 [170]	
	IM								
	SC	70 [164]				44			
	PO								
Cardiovascular	IV					8 [167]			
	IP								
	IM								
	SC		75 [166]						
	PO								
Antagonize 5-HT and Catechol Amines	IV				90 [167]	30 [168]	60 [167]		
	IP								
	IM								
	SC								
	PO								
Convulsant	IV								
	IP								
	IM							40 [161]	
	SC								
	PO								
	IV								
	IP								
	IM								
	SC								
	PO								

BW-467C60

(N-Benzyl-N'N''-dimethylguanidine)

mg/kg		Mouse	Rat	Guinea Pig	Rabbit	Cat	Dog	Monkey	
Lethal Dose Y–LD_{50} Z–MLD	IV	Y12 [171]							
	IP	Y150 [171]							
	IM								
	SC	Y260 [171]							
	PO	Y520 [171]							
Sympatholytic	IV				0.5 [171]	0.3 [171]	0.65 [171]	10 [171]	
	IP								
	IM								
	SC					2.5 [171]			
	PO					2.5 [171]	5 [171]		
Neuromuscular Block	IV					15 [171]	15 [171]	15 [171]	
	IP								
	IM								
	SC					100 [171]			
	PO								
	IV								
	IP								
	IM								
	SC								
	PO								

IN VITRO

mg %	Cardiac	Vascular	Gut	Uterine	Visceral	Skeletal		
Adrenolytic		*0.065 [171]						
Sympathomimetic		*0.3 [171]			1 [171]			

*Total mg

CAFFEINE

(Coffeine, Gluaranine, Methyltheobromine)

mg/kg		Mouse	Rat	Guinea Pig	Rabbit	Cat	Dog	Monkey	
Lethal Dose $Y-LD_{50}$ Z–MLD	IV	Y100 [172]	Y105 [172]		90 [109]	Z90 [109]	Y175 [183]		
	IP	250	Y245 [109]	Z235 [109]		Z190 [109]			
	IM				200 [182]				
	SC	185 [195]	Y250 [178]	Z220 [109]	275 [182]	150 [109]	110 [182]		
	PO		Y200		355 [182]	Z125 [109]	Z145 [109]		
CNS (Stimulant)	IV				25				
	IP	7.5 [174]	50 [179]						
	IM	20 [175]				*125 [24]	125 [24]		
	SC	20 [176]	15 [180]			*125 [24]	50 [24]		
	PO								
Antiseroton-ergic	IV			30 [92]					
	IP	20 [177]	40 [181]						
	IM								
	SC		40 [181]						
	PO								
Behavioral	IV								
	IP							200 [185]	
	IM								
	SC								
	PO								
Analeptic	IV				40		50		
	IP								
	IM								
	SC								
	PO								
EEG	IV					10 [184]			
	IP								
	IM								
	SC								
	PO								

*Total dose

mg/kg		Mouse	Rat	Guinea Pig	Rabbit	Cat	Dog	Monkey	
Decurariza-tion	IV					*210 7			
	IP								
	IM								
	SC								
	PO								
	IV								
	IP								
	IM								
	SC								
	PO								
	IV								
	IP								
	IM								
	SC								
	PO								
	IV								
	IP								
	IM								
	SC								
	PO								

*Total dose

IN VITRO

mg %	Cardiac	Vascular	Gut	Uterine	Visceral	Skeletal		
Antiserotonergic			10 92					

CALCIUM CHLORIDE

mg/kg		Mouse	Rat	Guinea Pig	Rabbit	Cat	Dog	Monkey	
Lethal Dose Y–LD_{50} Z–MLD	IV		Z169 [186]		274 [109]	249 [109]	274 [109]		
	IP		Y500 [187]						
	IM								
	SC				472 [109]	249 [109]	274 [109]		
	PO		Y4000 [187]		1384 [109]				
Convulsant	IV								
	IP								
	IM								
	SC		1000 [188]						
	PO								
Magnesium Sulfate Antagonist	IV				150				
	IP								
	IM								
	SC								
	PO								
	IV								
	IP								
	IM								
	SC								
	PO								

IN VITRO

mg %	Cardiac	Vascular	Gut	Uterine	Visceral	Skeletal		

CARBACHOL

(Carcholin, Moryl, Doryl)

mg/kg		Mouse	Rat	Guinea Pig	Rabbit	Cat	Dog	Monkey	
Lethal Dose Y–LD_{50} Z–MLD	IV	Y0.3 [13]	Y0.1 [13]	0.045 [189]					
	IP								
	IM								
	SC	Y3 [13]	Y4 [13]	0.08 [190]					
	PO	Y15 [13]	Y40 [13]						
Cholinergic	IV				0.002 [14]	0.03	0.03		
	IP								
	IM								
	SC				0.1 [14]		0.01 [14]		
	PO				2 [14]		0.25 [14]		
Nicotinic (Atropinized Animal)	IV					0.1	0.1		
	IP								
	IM								
	SC								
	PO								
	IV								
	IP								
	IM								
	SC								
	PO								

IN VITRO

mg %	Cardiac	Vascular	Gut	Uterine	Visceral	Skeletal		

CARISOPRODOL

(Soma, Somadril, Carisoma)

mg/kg		Mouse	Rat	Guinea Pig	Rabbit	Cat	Dog	Monkey	
Lethal Dose Y–LD_{50} Z–MLD	IV	165 [191]	Y450 [115]						
	IP								
	IM								
	SC								
	PO		Y1320 [115]						
Analgetic	IV	10 [191]			10 [191]				
	IP								
	IM								
	SC								
	PO		130 [117]	100 [192]					
Block EEG Desynchronization from Afferent Nerve Stimulation	IV				10	10 [193]			
	IP								
	IM								
	SC								
	PO								
Spinal Cord Depressant	IV						30 [191]		
	IP								
	IM								
	SC	100 [142]							
	PO								
Barbiturate Sleep Potentiation	IV								
	IP								
	IM								
	SC				100 [142]				
	PO			100 [142]					
	IV								
	IP								
	IM								
	SC								
	PO								

CHLORAL HYDRATE

(Notec, Somnos, Sontec)

mg/kg		Mouse	Rat	Guinea Pig	Rabbit	Cat	Dog	Monkey	
Lethal Dose $Y-LD_{50}$ Z-MLD	IV								
	IP	Z650 [194]	500						
	IM								
	SC	825 [195]	Y620 [196]		1000 [198]				
	PO		Y500 [197]		1400 [199]	Z440 [201]	1100 [203]		
Anesthetic	IV						125		
	IP	400	300 [197]						
	IM								
	SC						150		
	PO					250	500		
Cardiovascular and Respiratory	IV					25.8 [34]	125		
	IP								
	IM								
	SC								
	PO								
Behavioral and EEG	IV				30 [200]	30 [202]			
	IP								
	IM								
	SC								
	PO				30 [200]				
Increased Serotonin (Brain)	IV								
	IP		300 [31]						
	IM								
	SC								
	PO								
	IV								
	IP								
	IM								
	SC								
	PO								

α-CHLORALOSE

(Glucochloral, Chloralosane, Somio)

mg/kg		Mouse	Rat	Guinea Pig	Rabbit	Cat	Dog	Monkey	
Lethal Dose Y–LD_{50} Z–MLD	IV						120 [207]		
	IP	Y200 [204]				150 [207]			
	IM								
	SC		200		80 [206]				
	PO		400			600 [207]	600 [207]		
Anesthetic	IV				120	75 [208]	100 [209]		
	IP	114 [204]	55 [205]			50			
	IM								
	SC								
	PO								
Increased Serotonin (Brain)	IV								
	IP		100 [31]						
	IM								
	SC								
	PO								
	IV								
	IP								
	IM								
	SC								
	PO								

IN VITRO

mg %	Cardiac	Vascular	Gut	Uterine	Visceral	Skeletal		

CHLORDIAZEPOXIDE

(Librium)

mg/kg		Mouse	Rat	Guinea Pig	Rabbit	Cat	Dog	Monkey	
Lethal Dose Y–LD_{50} Z–MLD	IV	Y95 210	Y165 115						
	IP	Y268 210							
	IM								
	SC	Y530 210	Y800 210						
	PO	Y720 210	Y2000 115				Y1000		
Sedative	IV	30 211					*10 212		
	IP	50 211							
	IM								
	SC	94 211							
	PO	224 211	49 211			6 557	7.5 557	1 213	
Hypnotic	IV	72 211							
	IP	210 211							
	IM								
	SC	530 211							
	PO	740 211					80 213		
Anticonvulsant	IV							18	
	IP								
	IM								
	SC								
	PO	100 211							
Ataxic	IV								
	IP								
	IM								
	SC								
	PO						10 211	20 211	
	IV								
	IP								
	IM								
	SC								
	PO								

*Total dose

CHLORISONDAMINE

(Ecolid, SU-3088)

mg/kg		Mouse	Rat	Guinea Pig	Rabbit	Cat	Dog	Monkey	
Lethal Dose Y–LD50 Z–MLD	IV	Y24 [214]	Y28 [215]						
	IP								
	IM								
	SC								
	PO	Y401 [214]							
Ganglionic Block	IV					0.32 [215]	0.5		
	IP								
	IM								
	SC								
	PO						20 [215]		
Cardiovascular	IV		1.0 [216]		0.32 [216]		0.3 [215]	1.0 [216]	
	IP								
	IM								
	SC								
	PO								
	IV								
	IP								
	IM								
	SC								
	PO								

IN VITRO

mg %	Cardiac	Vascular	Gut	Uterine	Visceral	Skeletal		
Anticholinergic			1.0 [215]					

N-(2-CHLOROETHYL) DIBENZYLAMINE

(Dibenamine)

mg/kg		Mouse	Rat	Guinea Pig	Rabbit	Cat	Dog	Monkey	
Lethal Dose Y–LD_{50} Z–MLD	IV								
	IP								
	IM								
	SC	Y800 [217]							
	PO								
Adrenolytic	IV		20 [218]		50 [220]	30 [220]	15 [220]		
	IP		10 [219]						
	IM								
	SC								
	PO								
Inhibit Analeptic Effect of Amphetamine	IV				15				
	IP								
	IM								
	SC								
	PO								
	IV								
	IP								
	IM								
	SC								
	PO								

IN VITRO

mg %	Cardiac	Vascular	Gut	Uterine	Visceral	Skeletal		
Antiserotonergic			0.03 [92]					

CHLORPHENIRAMINE

(Chlor-Trimeton, Allergican, Piriton)

mg/kg		Mouse	Rat	Guinea Pig	Rabbit	Cat	Dog	Monkey	
Lethal Dose Y–LD_{50} Z–MLD	IV	39.6 [221]					98 [221]		
	IP	76.7 [221]							
	IM								
	SC	104.0 [221]		101.1 [221]					
	PO	142 [221]		186 [222]					
Antihistaminic	IV			1.16 [221]		0.1 [97]	5		
	IP								
	IM					0.1 [97]	0.1 [97]		
	SC			5			5		
	PO			0.13 [222]		0.1 [97]	0.1 [97]		
CNS (Stimulant)	IV								
	IP								
	IM								
	SC								
	PO	12 [222]				12 [222]			
	IV								
	IP								
	IM								
	SC								
	PO								

IN VITRO

mg %	Cardiac	Vascular	Gut	Uterine	Visceral	Skeletal		
Antihistaminic			0.0001 [223]					

mg/kg		Mouse	Rat	Guinea Pig	Rabbit	Cat	Dog	Monkey	
Lethal Dose Y–LD$_{50}$ Z–MLD	IV	Y26 [557]	Y29 [115]		Y16 [235]		Y30 [228]		
	IP	Y92 [82]	Y74 [228]						
	IM								
	SC		Y542 [82]						
	PO	Y319 [82]	Y493 [82]						
Sedative	IV				10 [236]	2.5 [97]	2.5 [97]	0.3 [248]	
	IP		8 [59]					5 [161]	
	IM					5 [557]	4 [557]	0.3 [248]	
	SC	25	20 [88]				4	0.63 [249]	
	PO					3.3 [97]	3.3 [97]	4.74 [250]	
Behavioral	IV				7 [60]		0.2 [243]		
	IP	6 [224]	4 [229]			17.5		5 [185]	
	IM	3 [175]	1 [230]				5 [244]		
	SC	10 [225]	5 [231]				1 [245]		
	PO	15.7 [226]	7 [232]				20 [246]	25	
EEG	IV				3 [237]	2 [239]	1 [247]	1 [247]	
	IP			5 [234]	0.5 [238]	15 [240]			
	IM								
	SC				5 [156]				
	PO								
Cardiovascular	IV		2.5 [218]		10 [236]	4 [241]	5 [88]		
	IP								
	IM					0.5 [242]			
	SC								
	PO								
Barbiturate Sleep Potentiation	IV	1	10 [233]						
	IP	4.1 [227]							
	IM								
	SC	50 [142]			25 [142]				
	PO			100 [105]					

mg/kg		Mouse	Rat	Guinea Pig	Rabbit	Cat	Dog	Monkey	
Anticonvulsant	IV								
	IP	20 [251]							
	IM								
	SC	60 [252]			5 [88]	2 [110]			
	PO	100 [142]							
Adrenolytic	IV		0.026 [253]				0.5		
	IP								
	IM						0.5		
	SC				50 [88]				
	PO						10		
Decreased Spontaneous Motor Neuron Activity	IV					1 [254]			
	IP								
	IM								
	SC								
	PO								
	IV								
	IP								
	IM								
	SC								
	PO								

IN VITRO

mg %	Cardiac	Vascular	Gut	Uterine	Visceral	Skeletal		
Langendorff	1.0 [88]							
Antiserotonergic			0.01 [92]					
Rabbit Atria	100 [88]							

CHLORTHIAZIDE

(Diuril, Saluric, Salisan)

mg/kg		Mouse	Rat	Guinea Pig	Rabbit	Cat	Dog	Monkey	
Lethal Dose Y–LD$_{50}$ Z–MLD	IV	Y1120 [58]					Y1000 [58]		
	IP	1400 [255]	Y1386 [58]						
	IM								
	SC								
	PO	Y8510 [58]	Y10000 [58]						
Diuretic	IV						6 [58]		
	IP		100 [58]						
	IM								
	SC								
	PO		100 [58]				3 [58]		
	IV								
	IP								
	IM								
	SC								
	PO								
	IV								
	IP								
	IM								
	SC								
	PO								

IN VITRO

mg %	Cardiac	Vascular	Gut	Uterine	Visceral	Skeletal		

COCAINE

mg/kg		Mouse	Rat	Guinea Pig	Rabbit	Cat	Dog	Monkey	
Lethal Dose Y–LD50 Z–MLD	IV	Z30 256	Y17.5 258	Z20 67	Y17 259	Z14.6 63			
	IP	Y150	Y70 259	Z60 67					
	IM								
	SC	100 257	Y250 259	Z50 67	Z126	Z31.9 63	Z35 63		
	PO								
Cardiovascular	IV			1	1 261	5	2 261		
	IP		20						
	IM						10 263		
	SC				1.5 7	20	20		
	PO								
CNS Stimulant	IV				1.3 262	1.3 262			
	IP	55 251							
	IM	10 175							
	SC	20 176							
	PO								
Convulsant	IV		10.5 260						
	IP								
	IM								
	SC				80				
	PO								
Counteract Bulbocapnine Catatonia	IV								
	IP								
	IM								
	SC							5 170	
	PO								
Decreased Norepinephrine in Heart, Spleen, and Adrenals	IV					5 91			
	IP								
	IM								
	SC								
	PO								

mg/kg		Mouse	Rat	Guinea Pig	Rabbit	Cat	Dog	Monkey	
Reserpine Antagonist	IV								
	IP	40 264							
	IM								
	SC								
	PO								
Pyretogenic	IV								
	IP								
	IM				25				
	SC								
	PO								
	IV								
	IP								
	IM								
	SC								
	PO								
	IV								
	IP								
	IM								
	SC								
	PO								

IN VITRO

mg %	Cardiac	Vascular	Gut	Uterine	Visceral	Skeletal		
Potentiate Epinephrine	0.05 265	0.01			1			
Block Dopamine	*0.008 266							
Antiserotonergic			10 92					

*Total mg

CODEINE

(Methylmorphine)

mg/kg		Mouse	Rat	Guinea Pig	Rabbit	Cat	Dog	Monkey	
Lethal Dose Y–LD_{50} Z–MLD	IV	Y68 [267]	Y55 [267]						
	IP	Y130 [17]	Y102 [268]						
	IM								
	SC	Y183 [267]	Y332 [267]		Y32 [270]				
	PO	Y395 [267]	Y542 [267]	Z120 [109]	100 [109]		200 [109]		
Analgetic	IV	25.5 [267]	6.2 [267]		10 [191]				
	IP	40	63						
	IM		14.8 [267]						
	SC	120	42				5		
	PO	97 [267]	22.5 [267]		10 [271]				
Antitussive	IV		10 [269]						
	IP								
	IM								
	SC		50 [269]				2.2 [24]		
	PO						2.2 [24]		
Decreased Motor Activity	IV	10 [191]							
	IP								
	IM								
	SC								
	PO								
Emetic	IV								
	IP								
	IM								
	SC						6.5 [267]		
	PO						5.0 [267]		
	IV								
	IP								
	IM								
	SC								
	PO								

mg/kg		Mouse	Rat	Guinea Pig	Rabbit	Cat	Dog	Monkey	
Lethal Dose Y–LD_{50} Z–MLD	IV		Y1.7 [275]		Z5.5 [277]	Y0.25 [279]			
	IP	Y3.5 [272]	4 [275]						
	IM								
	SC	Y3.1 [273]	Y4 [276]		Z7.5 [277]	0.8 [109]	0.57 [109]		
	PO	66.6 [272]				0.13 [109]	0.13 [109]		
Cardiovascular	IV					5 [275]			
	IP								
	IM								
	SC				15 [278]				
	PO								
Arrest Mitotic Division	IV								
	IP								
	IM								
	SC	2 [274]							
	PO								
	IV								
	IP								
	IM								
	SC								
	PO								

IN VITRO

mg %	Cardiac	Vascular	Gut	Uterine	Visceral	Skeletal		

CYPROHEPTADINE

(Periactin)

mg/kg		Mouse	Rat	Guinea Pig	Rabbit	Cat	Dog	Monkey	
Lethal Dose Y–LD_{50} Z–MLD	IV	Y23 [58]			4 [58]				
	IP	Y55 [58]	Y52 [58]						
	IM								
	SC	Y107 [58]							
	PO	Y125 [58]	Y295 [58]				50 [58]		
Antiserotonin	IV						0.1 [58]		
	IP								
	IM								
	SC		0.05 [58]						
	PO		0.08 [58]						
Antihistaminic	IV						0.05 [82]		
	IP			0.25 [58]					
	IM								
	SC								
	PO								
	IV								
	IP								
	IM								
	SC								
	PO								

IN VITRO

mg %	Cardiac	Vascular	Gut	Uterine	Visceral	Skeletal		
Antiserotonergic					4×10^{-5} [58]			

DECAMETHONIUM

(Syncurine, C10, Curam)

mg/kg		Mouse	Rat	Guinea Pig	Rabbit	Cat	Dog	Monkey	
Lethal Dose Y–LD_{50} Z–MLD	IV	Y0.75 [280]			Y0.2 [281]				
	IP								
	IM								
	SC								
	PO								
Neuromuscular Block	IV	0.17 [280]			0.1 [281]	0.015	0.2 [282]	0.1 [283]	
	IP								
	IM								
	SC								
	PO								
Behavioral	IV								
	IP		0.8 [61]						
	IM								
	SC								
	PO								
	IV								
	IP								
	IM								
	SC								
	PO								

IN VITRO

mg %	Cardiac	Vascular	Gut	Uterine	Visceral	Skeletal		

DEXAMPHETAMINE

(Dexedrine, Amsustain, Dephadren)

mg/kg		Mouse	Rat	Guinea Pig	Rabbit	Cat	Dog	Monkey	
Lethal Dose Y–LD_{50} Z–MLD	IV	Y14.3							
	IP	Y72.2 284							
	IM								
	SC	Y84 285	Y200						
	PO	Y37 82	Y80 82				Z6.4 82	Z32 82	
Cardiovascular	IV	0.4	0.4	0.4	0.4	0.35	0.4		
	IP								
	IM								
	SC								
	PO								
CNS Stimulant	IV				0.5 108	1.0 184	2.5		
	IP	10 286							
	IM								
	SC		3 180				2.5		
	PO		1 232						
Behavioral	IV				5 288				
	IP		2 287					0.2 185	
	IM							0.5 289	
	SC								
	PO		1 232						
Antagonize Adrenolytic Action of Bretylium	IV					0.35 153			
	IP								
	IM								
	SC								
	PO								
Analeptic	IV				10		20		
	IP								
	IM								
	SC								
	PO								

mg/kg		Mouse	Rat	Guinea Pig	Rabbit	Cat	Dog	Monkey	
EEG (Desynchronization)	IV								
	IP								
	IM								
	SC	10 [109]							
	PO								
Reverse Adrenergic Action of Guanethidine	IV					0.48 [285]			
	IP								
	IM								
	SC								
	PO								
	IV								
	IP								
	IM								
	SC								
	PO								
	IV								
	IP								
	IM								
	SC								
	PO								

IN VITRO

mg %	Cardiac	Vascular	Gut	Uterine	Visceral	Skeletal		
Rabbit		*0.004	0.1					

*Total mg

DIALLYL BARBITURIC ACID

(Dial, Allobarbital, Malilum)

mg/kg		Mouse	Rat	Guinea Pig	Rabbit	Cat	Dog	Monkey	
Lethal Dose	IV				70 [109]				
Y–LD_{50}	IP				Z100 [128]	100 [290]			
Z–MLD	IM								
	SC		Y110 [68]		100 [109]				
	PO			30 [76]	Z125 [128]				
Anesthetic	IV				50	36 [291]			
	IP					70 [292]			
	IM								
	SC		60 [66]						
	PO								
	IV								
	IP								
	IM								
	SC								
	PO								
	IV								
	IP								
	IM								
	SC								
	PO								

IN VITRO

mg %	Cardiac	Vascular	Gut	Uterine	Visceral	Skeletal		

DIBOZANE

(McN-181)

mg/kg		Mouse	Rat	Guinea Pig	Rabbit	Cat	Dog	Monkey	
Lethal Dose Y−LD_{50} Z−MLD	IV				Y43 293		60 293		
	IP	Y260 293							
	IM								
	SC								
	PO								
Adrenolytic	IV						2 294		
	IP								
	IM								
	SC								
	PO						1 293		
Sympatholytic	IV						3 295		
	IP								
	IM								
	SC								
	PO								
	IV								
	IP								
	IM								
	SC								
	PO								

IN VITRO

mg %	Cardiac	Vascular	Gut	Uterine	Visceral	Skeletal		
Adrenolytic					0.003			

DICHLOROISOPROTERENOL

(DCI)

mg/kg		Mouse	Rat	Guinea Pig	Rabbit	Cat	Dog	Monkey	
Lethal Dose Y–LD_{50} Z–MLD	IV	Y48 296							
	IP	Y132 296							
	IM								
	SC								
	PO								
Cardiovascular	IV				10	10 296	10 299		
	IP								
	IM								
	SC								
	PO								
Adrenolytic (β-Block)	IV		0.1 297		4 298	4 298	2 300		
	IP								
	IM								
	SC								
	PO								
	IV								
	IP								
	IM								
	SC								
	PO								

IN VITRO

mg %	Cardiac	Vascular	Gut	Uterine	Visceral	Skeletal		
Adrenolytic	0.04 301			1.0 296				
Sympathomimetic	0.65 302							

DIGITOXIN

(Digitaline, Crystodigin, Cardigin)

mg/kg		Mouse	Rat	Guinea Pig	Rabbit	Cat	Dog	Monkey	
Lethal Dose Y−LD_{50} Z−MLD	IV		12.2 74		3 303	0.35 303			
	IP								
	IM								
	SC	14 109				0.35 303	0.5 303		
	PO				100 303	0.25			
Cardiovascular	IV						0.15		
	IP								
	IM								
	SC						0.15		
	PO								
	IV								
	IP								
	IM								
	SC								
	PO								
	IV								
	IP								
	IM								
	SC								
	PO								

IN VITRO

mg %	Cardiac	Vascular	Gut	Uterine	Visceral	Skeletal		

DIGOXIN

(Lanoxin)

mg/kg		Mouse	Rat	Guinea Pig	Rabbit	Cat	Dog	Monkey	
Lethal Dose Y–LD_{50} Z–MLD	IV	20 [149]			3.56 [149]	0.35 [149]	0.3 [149]		
	IP		> 10 [149]						
	IM			0.6 [149]					
	SC			0.45 [149]					
	PO			1.8 [149]			0.3 [149]		
Cardiac Arrhythmia	IV					0.15 [149]	0.2 [149]		
	IP								
	IM								
	SC								
	PO								
	IV								
	IP								
	IM								
	SC								
	PO								
	IV								
	IP								
	IM								
	SC								
	PO								

IN VITRO

mg %	Cardiac	Vascular	Gut	Uterine	Visceral	Skeletal		

DIHYDROERGOTAMINE

(D.H.E. 45)

mg/kg		Mouse	Rat	Guinea Pig	Rabbit	Cat	Dog	Monkey	
Lethal Dose Y−LD_{50} Z−MLD	IV	Y118 304	Y110 304		Y25 304				
	IP								
	IM								
	SC					Y68 304			
	PO								
Adrenolytic	IV		0.5 218		1.0 305		10		
	IP								
	IM								
	SC								
	PO								
Sympatho-mimetic	IV						0.1 306		
	IP								
	IM								
	SC								
	PO								
	IV								
	IP								
	IM								
	SC								
	PO								

IN VITRO

mg %	Cardiac	Vascular	Gut	Uterine	Visceral	Skeletal		
Adrenolytic					0.02			

DIHYDROMORPHINONE

(Dilaudid, Laudicon, Hymorphan)

mg/kg		Mouse	Rat	Guinea Pig	Rabbit	Cat	Dog	Monkey	
Lethal Dose Y–LD_{50} Z–MLD	IV	Y88 [307]							
	IP								
	IM								
	SC	Y84 [308]							
	PO								
Anesthetic	IV						3.5 [557]		
	IP								
	IM								
	SC						7.5 [557]		
	PO								
Analgetic	IV		1.32 [269]						
	IP	0.25 [309]	1.7 [269]	3.1 [309]					
	IM					0.26 [310]			
	SC		0.9 [269]				2		
	PO		18 [269]						
Behavioral	IV						10		
	IP		7.1 [310]						
	IM								
	SC								
	PO								
Catatonic	IV								
	IP		4 [269]						
	IM								
	SC								
	PO								
	IV								
	IP								
	IM								
	SC								
	PO								

DIISOPROPYL-FLUOROPHOSPHATE

(DFP, Floropryl, Diflupyl)

mg/kg		Mouse	Rat	Guinea Pig	Rabbit	Cat	Dog	Monkey	
Lethal Dose Y–LD_{50} Z–MLD	IV				Y0.34 311	Y1.63 311	Y3.43 311	Y0.25 311	
	IP								
	IM		Y1.82 311						
	SC	Y3.71 311	Y3.0 311		Y1.0 311		Y3.0 311		
	PO	Y36.8 311	Y6.0 311		Y9.78 311				
Anticholine-esterase	IV								
	IP								
	IM		1 312				1 312	0.20 312	
	SC								
	PO							0.50 312	
Sedative	IV								
	IP								
	IM		1 312				2 312		
	SC								
	PO								
	IV								
	IP								
	IM								
	SC								
	PO								

IN VITRO

mg %	Cardiac	Vascular	Gut	Uterine	Visceral	Skeletal		

DIMETHINDENE

(Forhistal)

mg/kg		Mouse	Rat	Guinea Pig	Rabbit	Cat	Dog	Monkey	
Lethal Dose Y−LD_{50} Z−MLD	IV		Y26.8 [93]				Y45 [93]		
	IP								
	IM								
	SC								
	PO		Y618.2 [93]	Y888 [93]					
Antihistaminic	IV								
	IP								
	IM								
	SC								
	PO			0.06 [93]					
Cardiovascular	IV						9 [93]		
	IP								
	IM								
	SC								
	PO								
	IV								
	IP								
	IM								
	SC								
	PO								

IN VITRO

mg %	Cardiac	Vascular	Gut	Uterine	Visceral	Skeletal		
Antihistaminic			0.0007 [93]					
Anticholinergic			0.4 [93]					

2,4-DINITROPHENOL

(α-Dinitrophenol, Alfiden)

mg/kg		Mouse	Rat	Guinea Pig	Rabbit	Cat	Dog	Monkey	
Lethal Dose Y–LD_{50} Z–MLD	IV						Y30 [315]		
	IP				100 [318]				
	IM						Y20 [315]		
	SC		Y25 [315]		30 [315]		Y22 [315]		
	PO		Y30 [316]		Y200 [318]		Y25 [315]		
Hyperthermic	IV						5 [319]		
	IP				10 [120]				
	IM						5 [319]		
	SC		10 [317]		20 [319]		5 [319]		
	PO						5 [319]		
Respiratory	IV						20 [319]		
	IP								
	IM				20 [319]				
	SC				20 [311]				
	PO								
	IV								
	IP								
	IM								
	SC								
	PO								

IN VITRO

mg %	Cardiac	Vascular	Gut	Uterine	Visceral	Skeletal		

DIPHEN HYDRAMINE

(Benadryl, Dimedrol, Amidryl)

mg/kg		Mouse	Rat	Guinea Pig	Rabbit	Cat	Dog	Monkey	
Lethal Dose Y–LD_{50} Z–MLD	IV	Y31	Y42 321		Y10 321		Y24 321		
	IP	Y84 320	Y82 324	Y75 324					
	IM								
	SC	Y127 321	Y475 321	40.2 221					
	PO	Y164 321	Y500 325	284 221					
Antihistaminic	IV			23 221		1.8 97	1.8 97		
	IP			12.5					
	IM					1.8 97	1.8 97		
	SC			5					
	PO						2.2 97		
Anticonvulsant	IV								
	IP	30 251							
	IM	15.7 140							
	SC								
	PO	30 322	25 326						
CNS (EEG Synchroniza- tion)	IV				15 108				
	IP								
	IM								
	SC								
	PO								
Behavioral	IV								
	IP	40 323							
	IM								
	SC								
	PO								
	IV								
	IP								
	IM								
	SC								
	PO								

DMPP

(Dimethyl phenal piperazine)

mg/kg		Mouse	Rat	Guinea Pig	Rabbit	Cat	Dog	Monkey	
Lethal Dose Y–LD_{50} Z–MLD	IV				1 [314]		20 [313]		
	IP	Y40 [313]							
	IM	Y27.5 [314]							
	SC								
	PO	Y365 [313]	Y2000 [313]						
Ganglionic Stimulant	IV					0.2 [314]	0.15 [314]		
	IP								
	IM								
	SC								
	PO								
Cardiovascular	IV				20 [313]	0.25 [313]	2 [313]		
	IP								
	IM								
	SC								
	PO								
	IV								
	IP								
	IM								
	SC								
	PO								

IN VITRO

mg %	Cardiac	Vascular	Gut	Uterine	Visceral	Skeletal		
Langendorff	*0.025 [314]							
Guinea Pig			0.4 [314]					

*Total mg

DOPA

(Dihydroxyphenylalanine)

mg/kg		Mouse	Rat	Guinea Pig	Rabbit	Cat	Dog	Monkey	
Lethal Dose Y–LD50 Z–MLD	IV								
	IP		*10 328						
	IM								
	SC								
	PO								
Behavioral	IV				25 14				
	IP	750 327	20 329						
	IM								
	SC								
	PO								
Cardiovascular	IV		12 328						
	IP		12 328						
	IM								
	SC								
	PO								
	IV								
	IP								
	IM								
	SC								
	PO								

*Total dose

IN VITRO

mg %	Cardiac	Vascular	Gut	Uterine	Visceral	Skeletal		

DOPAMINE

(3-hydroxytyramine)

mg/kg		Mouse	Rat	Guinea Pig	Rabbit	Cat	Dog	Monkey	
Lethal Dose Y–LD_{50} Z–MLD	IV								
	IP								
	IM								
	SC								
	PO								
Cardiovascular	IV			*0.08 330	*0.8 330	*0.16 330	0.15 330		
	IP								
	IM								
	SC								
	PO								
EEG (desynchronization)	IV				15 331				
	IP								
	IM								
	SC								
	PO								
	IV								
	IP								
	IM								
	SC								
	PO								

*Total dose

IN VITRO

mg %	Cardiac	Vascular	Gut	Uterine	Visceral	Skeletal		
Rabbit	0.16 266	100 330	0.024 266					
Cat	*5 266		0.164 266	0.26 266				
Hind Limb (Perfusion)		*0.64						

*Total mg

EDROPHONIUM

(Tensilon, RO2-3198)

mg/kg		Mouse	Rat	Guinea Pig	Rabbit	Cat	Dog	Monkey	
Lethal Dose Y–LD_{50} Z–MLD	IV	Y9 210			Y28.5 210		Y15 250		
	IP	Y37 210							
	IM								
	SC	Y130 210							
	PO	Y600 210							
Curare Antagonist	IV					0.4	0.4		
	IP								
	IM								
	SC		2.5						
	PO								
Muscle Relaxant	IV					0.5	0.5		
	IP								
	IM								
	SC								
	PO								
	IV								
	IP								
	IM								
	SC								
	PO								

IN VITRO

mg %	Cardiac	Vascular	Gut	Uterine	Visceral	Skeletal		

EPHEDRINE

(Ephedral, Sanedrine, Biophedrin)

mg/kg		Mouse	Rat	Guinea Pig	Rabbit	Cat	Dog	Monkey	
Lethal Dose Y–LD_{50} Z–MLD	IV	200 [6]	Z137 [334]		Z60 [6]	Z60 [6]	Z72.5 [333]		
	IP	Z400 [332]	800 [335]		Z355 [334]				
	IM				Z340 [333]				
	SC	500 [333]	Y650	400 [6]	Z360 [333]		Z220 [333]		
	PO	400 [6]	Z160 [335]		Z590 [334]				
Behavioral	IV							15	
	IP	1.25 [177]							
	IM								
	SC								
	PO		100 [336]				0.06 [337]		
Cardiovascular	IV		1	1	1	1	0.5		
	IP								
	IM								
	SC								
	PO								
CNS Stimulant	IV						2.5		
	IP						3.3 [97]		
	IM								
	SC						2.5		
	PO						*20 [97]		
Antagonize Adrenolytic Action of Bretylium	IV					0.35 [153]			
	IP								
	IM								
	SC								
	PO								
Antagonize Reserpine Ptosis	IV								
	IP	20 [78]							
	IM								
	SC								
	PO								

*Total mg

EPHEDRINE (continued)

mg/kg		Mouse	Rat	Guinea Pig	Rabbit	Cat	Dog	Monkey	
Increase Rate of Amine Catachol Disappearance	IV								
	IP	50 338							
	IM								
	SC								
	PO								
Hyperthermic	IV								
	IP								
	IM								
	SC		60 259						
	PO								
	IV								
	IP								
	IM								
	SC								
	PO								
	IV								
	IP								
	IM								
	SC								
	PO								

IN VITRO

mg %	Cardiac	Vascular	Gut	Uterine	Visceral	Skeletal		
Antiserotonergic								
Rat			0.8 92					
Guinea Pig			0.3 92					
Rabbit Ear		*0.016 339						

*Total mg

EPINEPHRINE

(Adrenalin, Suprarenin, Suprarenaline)

mg/kg		Mouse	Rat	Guinea Pig	Rabbit	Cat	Dog	Monkey	
Lethal Dose Y–LD_{50} Z–MLD	IV		Y0.98	0.15 [341]	0.2 [341]	0.7 [341]	0.15 [341]		
	IP	Y4 [340]	10 [343]						
	IM		Y3.5 [7]						
	SC	Y1.47 [341]	Y5.0 [341]	1.5 [341]	15 [341]	20 [341]	5.5 [341]		
	PO	Y50	30 [341]		30 [341]				
Cardiovascular	IV		0.003	0.003	0.003	0.003	0.003		
	IP								
	IM						0.05		
	SC						0.05		
	PO								
Behavioral	IV						0.05 [99]		
	IP	2.5 [177]	1 [344]						
	IM								
	SC								
	PO								
CNS	IV				0.01 [345]				
	IP								
	IM								
	SC								
	PO								
Barbiturate Sleep Potentiation	IV								
	IP	2 [342]							
	IM	0.4 [7]							
	SC								
	PO								
Antagonize Reserpine Ptosis	IV								
	IP	1 [78]							
	IM								
	SC								
	PO								

EPINEPHRINE (continued)

mg/kg		Mouse	Rat	Guinea Pig	Rabbit	Cat	Dog	Monkey	
Diuretic	IV								
	IP								
	IM								
	SC		0.5 [151]						
	PO								
	IV								
	IP								
	IM								
	SC								
	PO								
	IV								
	IP								
	IM								
	SC								
	PO								
	IV								
	IP								
	IM								
	SC								
	PO								

IN VITRO

mg %	Cardiac	Vascular	Gut	Uterine	Visceral	Skeletal		
Sympathomimetic	0.01	0.003	0.01	0.02	0.01			
Langendorff	*0.1							
Antiserotonergic			0.002 [92]					

*Total mg

ERGONOVINE

(Ergotrate, Cornocentin, Ermetrine)

mg/kg		Mouse	Rat	Guinea Pig	Rabbit	Cat	Dog	Monkey	
Lethal Dose Y–LD_{50} Z–MLD	IV	145 [346]		80 [346]	Z7.5				
	IP								
	IM								
	SC		0.5 [346]						
	PO								
Oxytocic	IV						*0.35 [97]		
	IP								
	IM						*0.35 [97]		
	SC		500 [257]						
	PO								
Antagonize Epinephrine Toxicity	IV		0.085						
	IP								
	IM								
	SC								
	PO								
	IV								
	IP								
	IM								
	SC								
	PO								

*Total dose

IN VITRO

mg %	Cardiac	Vascular	Gut	Uterine	Visceral	Skeletal		
Oxytocic				50 [347]				

ERGOTAMINE

(Gynergen, Femergin, Ergomar)

mg/kg		Mouse	Rat	Guinea Pig	Rabbit	Cat	Dog	Monkey	
Lethal Dose Y–LD_{50} Z–MLD	IV	Y52 [348]	Y62 [304]	36 [351]	Y3.55 [352]				
	IP								
	IM								
	SC		Z125 [349]			Y11 [352]			
	PO								
Adrenolytic	IV				0.15 [352]	1	8 [354]		
	IP								
	IM								
	SC								
	PO								
CNS	IV					0.1 [353]			
	IP								
	IM								
	SC		5 [350]						
	PO								
	IV								
	IP								
	IM								
	SC								
	PO								

IN VITRO

mg %	Cardiac	Vascular	Gut	Uterine	Visceral	Skeletal		
Rabbit				0.5 [352]				
Guinea Pig				0.002 [352]				

FLUOROACETIC ACID

(Fluoroacetate, Prodenticide 1080)

mg/kg		Mouse	Rat	Guinea Pig	Rabbit	Cat	Dog	Monkey	
Lethal Dose Y–LD_{50} Z–MLD	IV				Y0.25 [346]	Y0.2 [346]	Y0.06 [346]	Y4 [346]	
	IP	Y10 [346]	Y0.4 [346]	Y0.35 [346]					
	IM		Y5 [346]						
	SC	Y16 [346]	Y2.5 [346]	0.25 [346]	0.75 [346]				
	PO	Y8 [346]	Y2.5 [346]						
Decreased Mitotic Index of Mucosal Epithelium	IV						1.0 [355]		
	IP								
	IM								
	SC								
	PO								
	IV								
	IP								
	IM								
	SC								
	PO								
	IV								
	IP								
	IM								
	SC								
	PO								

IN VITRO

mg %	Cardiac	Vascular	Gut	Uterine	Visceral	Skeletal		
Rabbit			0.004 [356]					

GAMMA-AMINOBUTYRIC ACID

(GABA)

mg/kg		Mouse	Rat	Guinea Pig	Rabbit	Cat	Dog	Monkey	
Lethal Dose Y–LD_{50} Z–MLD	IV								
	IP								
	IM								
	SC								
	PO								
Cardiovascular	IV				3.0 208	10 208	3.0 208		
	IP								
	IM								
	SC								
	PO								
CNS (Inhibition)	IV					0.1 357	100 358		
	IP								
	IM								
	SC								
	PO								
Behavioral	IV	1000 359							
	IP								
	IM								
	SC								
	PO	400 359							
	IV								
	IP								
	IM								
	SC								
	PO								
	IV								
	IP								
	IM								
	SC								
	PO								

GALLAMINE

(Flaxedil, Relaxan, Tricuran)

mg/kg		Mouse	Rat	Guinea Pig	Rabbit	Cat	Dog	Monkey	
Lethal Dose Y–LD_{50} Z–MLD	IV	Y4.3	Y5.5 361		Y0.65 361		Y0.8 361		
	IP								
	IM				Y2.5 361				
	SC	Y17.4 360	Y25 361		Y3.0 361				
	PO	Y425 361			Y100 361				
Neuromuscular Block	IV				0.6 88	5 362	0.4 361		
	IP								
	IM				0.75 361				
	SC				1.5 361				
	PO								
	IV								
	IP								
	IM								
	SC								
	PO								
	IV								
	IP								
	IM								
	SC								
	PO								

IN VITRO

mg %	Cardiac	Vascular	Gut	Uterine	Visceral	Skeletal		

GUANETHIDINE

(Ismelin, SU-5864)

mg/kg		Mouse	Rat	Guinea Pig	Rabbit	Cat	Dog	Monkey	
Lethal Dose Y–LD_{50} Z–MLD	IV	Y22 93	Y23 363		50	50			
	IP								
	IM								
	SC								
	PO		Y1000 363						
Autonomic Effects	IV				3	15 363	15		
	IP					15 367			
	IM								
	SC					7.5 171			
	PO					15 171	35 93		
Catechol Amine Depletion	IV		5 150		12.5 366	15 91			
	IP		8 364						
	IM		25 150						
	SC		15 365			15 366			
	PO								
	IV								
	IP								
	IM								
	SC								
	PO								

IN VITRO

mg %	Cardiac	Vascular	Gut	Uterine	Visceral	Skeletal		
Finkleman 812			0.4 365					

HARMALINE

(3,4-dihydroharmine)

mg/kg		Mouse	Rat	Guinea Pig	Rabbit	Cat	Dog	Monkey	
Lethal Dose Y–LD_{50} Z–MLD	IV								
	IP								
	IM								
	SC	Y120 [115]	Z120 [368]	Z100 [368]	Z100 [368]	Z100 [368]	33.3 [368]		
	PO								
Cardiovascular and Uterine	IV				10 [371]	1 [368]	5		
	IP								
	IM								
	SC								
	PO								
Behavioral	IV								
	IP		5 [370]						
	IM								
	SC		2.5						
	PO								
Ataxic	IV								
	IP	15 [369]	10						
	IM								
	SC			10 [368]					
	PO								
Spinal Reflex Depressant	IV					5 [372]			
	IP								
	IM								
	SC								
	PO								
	IV								
	IP								
	IM								
	SC								
	PO								

HARMINE

(Banisterine, Yageine, Telepathine)

mg/kg		Mouse	Rat	Guinea Pig	Rabbit	Cat	Dog	Monkey	
Lethal Dose Y–LD_{50} Z–MLD	IV								
	IP								
	IM								
	SC	300 373	Z200 374	100 375	200 375	Z200 373		Z30 373	
	PO								
Cardiovascular	IV				10 374	4 374	5		
	IP								
	IM								
	SC								
	PO								
Tremor	IV								
	IP	15 369							
	IM	10 175							
	SC								
	PO								
Behavioral	IV								
	IP								
	IM	1 175							
	SC								
	PO								
Ganglionic Block	IV					25 376	15 376		
	IP								
	IM								
	SC								
	PO								
	IV								
	IP								
	IM								
	SC								
	PO								

HEMICHOLINIUM
(HC-3)

mg/kg		Mouse	Rat	Guinea Pig	Rabbit	Cat	Dog	Monkey	
Lethal Dose Y–LD_{50} Z–MLD	IV					1 378			
	IP	Y0.064 377							
	IM								
	SC								
	PO								
Parasympatholytic	IV				5.9 377		0.013 377		
	IP								
	IM								
	SC								
	PO								
Decreased Spinal Cord Inhibition	IV					3.5 379			
	IP								
	IM								
	SC								
	PO								
	IV								
	IP								
	IM								
	SC								
	PO								

IN VITRO

mg %	Cardiac	Vascular	Gut	Uterine	Visceral	Skeletal		
Guinea Pig						20 100		
Rat						20		
Rabbit	4 100			2.4 100				
Cat	50 100							

HEPARIN

(Panheparin, Liguemin, Pularin)

mg/kg		Mouse	Rat	Guinea Pig	Rabbit	Cat	Dog	Monkey	
Lethal Dose Y–LD_{50} Z–MLD	IV	Y1780 [380]							
	IP								
	IM								
	SC								
	PO								
Anticoagulant	IV		10 [381]		5 [383]	5 [385]	8 [209]	2	
	IP								
	IM								
	SC								
	PO								
Increased Lipoproeteinase Activity	IV		6 [382]		1.5 [384]				
	IP								
	IM								
	SC								
	PO								
	IV								
	IP								
	IM								
	SC								
	PO								

IN VITRO

mg %	Cardiac	Vascular	Gut	Uterine	Visceral	Skeletal		

HEXAMETHONIUM

(C6, Hexameton, Bistrium)

mg/kg		Mouse	Rat	Guinea Pig	Rabbit	Cat	Dog	Monkey	
Lethal Dose Y–LD_{50} Z–MLD	IV	Y21 [214]							
	IP	Y42 [214]							
	IM								
	SC								
	PO	Y484 [214]							
Ganglionic Block	IV		20 [386]	5	10	10	10		
	IP		2.8 [387]						
	IM								
	SC								
	PO		100 [387]						
CNS	IV								
	IP	5 [350]							
	IM								
	SC		2 [350]						
	PO								
	IV								
	IP								
	IM								
	SC								
	PO								

IN VITRO

mg %	Cardiac	Vascular	Gut	Uterine	Visceral	Skeletal		
Rat			0.24 [388]					
Rabbit	10		5					

HEXOBARBITAL

(Evipan, Cyclonal, Privenal)

mg/kg		Mouse	Rat	Guinea Pig	Rabbit	Cat	Dog	Monkey	
Lethal Dose $Y-LD_{50}$ Z-MLD	IV	190 [389]			Y80 [66]	100 [66]	100 [66]		
	IP	Y340 [390]	Y280 [393]	100 [66]	Z225 [393]				
	IM								
	SC	250 [66]	404 [66]						
	PO	Y468 [391]	Y468		Z1200 [394]	400 [66]			
Anesthetic	IV	47 [392]			25	25 [66]	30 [66]		
	IP	75	75 [393]		40 [395]	40 [395]			
	IM								
	SC	150 [66]	90 [66]						
	PO	150 [66]				100 [66]			
Increased Brain Serotonin	IV								
	IP		100 [31]						
	IM								
	SC								
	PO								
Increased Spontaneous Motor Activity	IV								
	IP	26 [204]							
	IM								
	SC								
	PO								
Decreased Hippocampal Seizure	IV					20 [396]			
	IP								
	IM								
	SC								
	PO								
	IV								
	IP								
	IM								
	SC								
	PO								

HEXOCYCLIUM

(Tral)

mg/kg		Mouse	Rat	Guinea Pig	Rabbit	Cat	Dog	Monkey	
Lethal Dose Y–LD_{50} Z–MLD	IV	Y10.5 [111]							
	IP	Y55 [111]							
	IM								
	SC	Y360 [111]							
	PO	Y600 [111]							
Anticholinergic	IV					4 [111]	5 [111]		
	IP								
	IM								
	SC								
	PO								
Antispasmodic	IV						0.04 [111]		
	IP								
	IM								
	SC								
	PO								
	IV								
	IP								
	IM								
	SC								
	PO								

IN VITRO

mg %	Cardiac	Vascular	Gut	Uterine	Visceral	Skeletal		

HISTAMINE

(Eramin, Ergamine, Ergotidine)

mg/kg		Mouse	Rat	Guinea Pig	Rabbit	Cat	Dog	Monkey	
Lethal Dose Y–LD_{50} Z–MLD	IV			Y0.18 [398]	0.1 [109]		30	50 [109]	
	IP			33 [399]					
	IM								
	SC	2500 [195]		7 [399]	13.5 [399]				
	PO			300 [400]					
Cardiovascular	IV			0.1	0.15	0.005	0.005		
	IP								
	IM								
	SC						1		
	PO								
Increase Stomach HCl	IV								
	IP								
	IM								
	SC						*0.1		
	PO		25 [397]				0.5 [397]		
	IV								
	IP								
	IM								
	SC								
	PO								

*Total dose

IN VITRO

mg %	Cardiac	Vascular	Gut	Uterine	Visceral	Skeletal		
Guinea Pig			0.005	0.005				
Rabbit	0.1			0.5				

HOMATROPINE

(Malcotran, Mesopin, Novatropine)

mg/kg		Mouse	Rat	Guinea Pig	Rabbit	Cat	Dog	Monkey	
Lethal Dose Y–LD_{50} Z–MLD	IV								
	IP	Y60 101	Y82 101	Y120 101					
	IM								
	SC	Y650 101	Y800 101						
	PO	Y1400 101	Y1200 101	Y1000 101					
Anticholinergic	IV								
	IP								
	IM				0.16 101				
	SC	0.13 101	27 101						
	PO	12 101	18 101						
Ganglionic Block	IV					1.0 101			
	IP								
	IM								
	SC								
	PO								
	IV								
	IP								
	IM								
	SC								
	PO								

IN VITRO

mg %	Cardiac	Vascular	Gut	Uterine	Visceral	Skeletal		
Rabbit			0.01					

HORDENINE

(Anhaline)

mg/kg		Mouse	Rat	Guinea Pig	Rabbit	Cat	Dog	Monkey	
Lethal Dose Y–LD_{50} Z–MLD	IV			300 401	275 109		275 109		
	IP								
	IM								
	SC		1000 401	2000 401					
	PO						2000 109		
Cardiovascular	IV					*2 402			
	IP								
	IM								
	SC								
	PO								
Block Diarrhea	IV								
	IP								
	IM								
	SC						35 274		
	PO								
	IV								
	IP								
	IM								
	SC								
	PO								

*Total dose

IN VITRO

mg %	Cardiac	Vascular	Gut	Uterine	Visceral	Skeletal		
Stimulation			0.8 402	0.8 402				

1-HYDRAZINOPHTHALAZINE

(Apresoline, Hydralazine)

mg/kg		Mouse	Rat	Guinea Pig	Rabbit	Cat	Dog	Monkey	
Lethal Dose Y–LD_{50} Z–MLD	IV		34 [403]				64 [817]		
	IP	Y83 [817]							
	IM								
	SC								
	PO		173 [93]						
Cardiovascular	IV		1.0 [403]	1.0 [403]		1.0 [403]	1.0 [403]		
	IP		2.6 [404]						
	IM								
	SC								
	PO								
Adrenolytic	IV					1.0 [405]	8.0 [817]		
	IP								
	IM								
	SC								
	PO								
	IV								
	IP								
	IM								
	SC								
	PO								

IN VITRO

mg %	Cardiac	Vascular	Gut	Uterine	Visceral	Skeletal		
Spasmogenic			10 [403]					

HYDROCHLOROTHIAZIDE

(Esidrex, Hydro-Diuril, Oretic)

mg/kg		Mouse	Rat	Guinea Pig	Rabbit	Cat	Dog	Monkey	
Lethal Dose Y–LD_{50} Z–MLD	IV	Y884 58			Y461 58		Y250 58		
	IP	Y578 58	Y234 58						
	IM								
	SC	Y1470 58	Y1270 58						
	PO	Y3080 58	Y6190 58						
Diuretic	IV						0.5 58		
	IP		15 58						
	IM								
	SC								
	PO		15 58				0.25 58	10 58	
	IV								
	IP								
	IM								
	SC								
	PO								
	IV								
	IP								
	IM								
	SC								
	PO								

IN VITRO

mg %	Cardiac	Vascular	Gut	Uterine	Visceral	Skeletal		

ρ-HYDROXY-α-(METHYLAMINOMETHYL) BENZYL ALCOHOL

(Araleptin, Sympatol, Synephrin)

mg/kg		Mouse	Rat	Guinea Pig	Rabbit	Cat	Dog	Monkey	
Lethal Dose Y–LD_{50} Z–MLD	IV								
	IP								
	IM								
	SC	750 406							
	PO								
Cardiovascular	IV					*0.7 266	0.25 408		
	IP								
	IM								
	SC								
	PO								
Decrease Catechol Amine Binding	IV								
	IP	40 338							
	IM								
	SC								
	PO								
Oxytocic	IV		2.5 407						
	IP								
	IM								
	SC								
	PO								
	IV								
	IP								
	IM								
	SC								
	PO								
	IV								
	IP								
	IM								
	SC								
	PO								

*Total dose

L-3-HYDROXY-N-METHYLMORPHINAN

(Levorphanol, Levo-Dromoran, Levorfan)

mg/kg		Mouse	Rat	Guinea Pig	Rabbit	Cat	Dog	Monkey	
Lethal Dose	IV	Y41.5 [210]			Y20 [210]				
Y–LD_{50}	IP								
Z–MLD	IM								
	SC	Y187 [210]	Y110 [210]						
	PO	Y285 [210]	Y150 [210]						
Analgetic	IV								
	IP								
	IM								
	SC		2.0 [435]				2		
	PO								
Respiratory	IV				0.5 [435]				
	IP								
	IM								
	SC								
	PO								
Antitussive	IV						2 [435]		
	IP								
	IM								
	SC								
	PO								
	IV								
	IP								
	IM								
	SC								
	PO								
	IV								
	IP								
	IM								
	SC								
	PO								

DL-3-HYDROXY-N-METHYLMORPHINAN

(Dromoran, Methorphinan, Racemorphan)

mg/kg		Mouse	Rat	Guinea Pig	Rabbit	Cat	Dog	Monkey	
Lethal Dose Y–LD_{50} Z–MLD	IV	41 409			19 409				
	IP	120 409							
	IM								
	SC	153 409	125 409						
	PO								
Analgetic	IV								
	IP								
	IM								
	SC		1.0 409						
	PO		10 409						
Respiratory Depressant	IV				2.0 409				
	IP								
	IM								
	SC								
	PO								
Increased Intestinal Motility	IV						2 409		
	IP								
	IM								
	SC								
	PO								
Cardiovascular	IV					4 409	4 409		
	IP								
	IM								
	SC								
	PO								
	IV								
	IP								
	IM								
	SC								
	PO								

5-HYDROXYTRYPTOPHANE
(5-HTP)

mg/kg		Mouse	Rat	Guinea Pig	Rabbit	Cat	Dog	Monkey	
Lethal Dose Y−LD_{50} Z−MLD	IV								
	IP								
	IM								
	SC								
	PO								
Behavioral	IV	25 [286]	25 [411]						
	IP	100 [204]							
	IM								
	SC		40 [286]						
	PO								
CNS	IV				65 [410]	100 [412]	50 [410]		
	IP	45 [410]	75 [410]						
	IM								
	SC								
	PO								
Gastrointestinal Stimulant	IV					60 [410]	60 [410]		
	IP	60 [410]	60 [410]						
	IM								
	SC								
	PO								
Cardiovascular	IV				87.5 [410]		30 [413]		
	IP								
	IM								
	SC								
	PO								
Anticonvulsant	IV								
	IP								
	IM								
	SC		30 [414]						
	PO								

mg/kg		Mouse	Rat	Guinea Pig	Rabbit	Cat	Dog	Monkey	
Decreased Motor Activity	IV					50 410	30 413		
	IP								
	IM								
	SC								
	PO								
	IV								
	IP								
	IM								
	SC								
	PO								
	IV								
	IP								
	IM								
	SC								
	PO								
	IV								
	IP								
	IM								
	SC								
	PO								

IN VITRO

mg %	Cardiac	Vascular	Gut	Uterine	Visceral	Skeletal		

HYDROXYZINE

(Atarax, Placidol, Tran-Q)

mg/kg		Mouse	Rat	Guinea Pig	Rabbit	Cat	Dog	Monkey	
Lethal Dose	IV	137 [117]	Y45						
Y–LD_{50}	IP	137 [117]	137 [117]						
Z–MLD	IM								
	SC								
	PO	515 [226]	500 [117]						
Behavioral	IV							10 [418]	
	IP	70 [137]	20 [416]				0.1 [417]		
	IM	250 [175]							
	SC	100 [415]							
	PO								
Tolerated	IV							12.5 [117]	
	IP								
	IM								
	SC								
	PO	490 [226]					20 [117]	87.5 [117]	
Barbiturate Sleep Potentiation	IV								
	IP								
	IM								
	SC	50 [142]		50 [142]	50 [142]				
	PO								
Analgetic	IV								
	IP								
	IM								
	SC			50 [142]					
	PO			100 [142]					
EEG (Synchronization)	IV				6 [108]				
	IP								
	IM								
	SC								
	PO								

mg/kg		Mouse	Rat	Guinea Pig	Rabbit	Cat	Dog	Monkey	
Cardiovascular	IV						7.5 [419]		
	IP								
	IM								
	SC								
	PO								
Antidiuretic	IV						5 [420]		
	IP								
	IM								
	SC								
	PO								
	IV								
	IP								
	IM								
	SC								
	PO								
	IV								
	IP								
	IM								
	SC								
	PO								

IN VITRO

mg %	Cardiac	Vascular	Gut	Uterine	Visceral	Skeletal		

ILIDAR

(Azepine, Azapetine, RO-2-3248)

mg/kg		Mouse	Rat	Guinea Pig	Rabbit	Cat	Dog	Monkey	
Lethal Dose Y–LD_{50} Z–MLD	IV	Y27 210			Y28 210		Y50 210		
	IP	Y210 210							
	IM	Y600 421							
	SC	Y725 210							
	PO	Y460 210							
Adrenolytic (Cardiac)	IV						32 422		
	IP								
	IM								
	SC								
	PO								
Analgetic Hypothermic	IV								
	IP								
	IM								
	SC		100 421						
	PO								
Cardiovascular	IV						1 421		
	IP								
	IM								
	SC								
	PO						10 421		
Antifibrillatory	IV						3 421		
	IP								
	IM								
	SC								
	PO								
	IV								
	IP								
	IM								
	SC								
	PO								

IMIPRAMINE

(Tofranil, G22355, Imizin)

mg/kg		Mouse	Rat	Guinea Pig	Rabbit	Cat	Dog	Monkey	
Lethal Dose Y–LD_{50} Z–MLD	IV	Y35 [235]	Y22 [235]		Y18 [235]				
	IP	Y115 [59]							
	IM								
	SC								
	PO	Y400 [235]	Y625 [235]						
Barbiturate Sleep Potentiation	IV						5 [425]		
	IP								
	IM								
	SC	50 [423]			50 [142]				
	PO			25 [105]					
CNS	IV				10 [235]				
	IP		20 [59]						
	IM								
	SC	50 [235]	50 [235]			20 [235]			
	PO								
Antagonize Reserpine Ptosis	IV								
	IP	75 [264]	15 [810]						
	IM								
	SC								
	PO	100 [79]							
Cardiovascular	IV					1 [235]	4 [426]		
	IP								
	IM								
	SC								
	PO								
Decreased Motor Activity	IV								
	IP								
	IM								
	SC	50 [105]				10 [424]			
	PO								

IMIPRAMINE (continued)

mg/kg		Mouse	Rat	Guinea Pig	Rabbit	Cat	Dog	Monkey	
EEG	IV					40 [424]			
	IP								
	IM								
	SC								
	PO								
Decreased Catechol Amine Uptake	IV								
	IP					20 [91]			
	IM								
	SC								
	PO								
Serotonin and Catechol Amine Potentiation	IV					2.4 [427]			
	IP								
	IM								
	SC								
	PO								
	IV								
	IP								
	IM								
	SC								
	PO								

IN VITRO

mg %	Cardiac	Vascular	Gut	Uterine	Visceral	Skeletal		
Anticholinergic			*0.16 [235]					
Antihistiminic		*0.006 [235]						
Anti-$BaCl_2$			*0.3 [235]					
Antiserotonergic			*0.004 [235]					

*Total mg

IPRONIAZID

(Iprazid, Marsilid, RO-2-4572)

mg/kg		Mouse	Rat	Guinea Pig	Rabbit	Cat	Dog	Monkey	
Lethal Dose Y–LD_{50} Z–MLD	IV	Y725 [428]			Y150 [428]		140 [429]		
	IP	Y690 [428]							
	IM	Y683 [428]							
	SC	Y750 [428]							
	PO	Y968 [428]	Y383 [428]		Y150 [428]		140 [428]	640 [429]	
Monoamine Oxidase Inhibition	IV	100 [430]			100 [430]		65 [372]		
	IP	25 [429]	50 [429]						
	IM								
	SC	100 [430]			100 [430]	100 [430]			
	PO		100 [433]						
Increased Brain Serotonin and Norepinephrine	IV								
	IP	300 [431]	100 [148]						
	IM								
	SC		100 [434]		100				
	PO								
Barbiturate Sleep Potentiation	IV								
	IP	100 [411]							
	IM								
	SC	50 [142]		50 [142]	50 [142]				
	PO								
Cardiovascular	IV					8 [428]	163 [372]		
	IP								
	IM								
	SC								
	PO								
Behavioral	IV								
	IP								
	IM								
	SC	100 [432]	100 [370]						
	PO								

mg/kg		Mouse	Rat	Guinea Pig	Rabbit	Cat	Dog	Monkey	
Analgetic	IV								
	IP								
	IM								
	SC			50 142					
	PO								
Ganglionic Block	IV					100 376			
	IP								
	IM								
	SC								
	PO								
Decreased Motor Activity	IV								
	IP	200 204							
	IM								
	SC								
	PO								
	IV								
	IP								
	IM								
	SC								
	PO								

IN VITRO

mg %	Cardiac	Vascular	Gut	Uterine	Visceral	Skeletal		
Cat	10 429							

ISOCARBOXAZID

(Marplan, Marplon, RO-5-0831)

mg/kg		Mouse	Rat	Guinea Pig	Rabbit	Cat	Dog	Monkey	
Lethal Dose Y–LD_{50} Z–MLD	IV								
	IP	Y110 [210]	Y199 [210]						
	IM								
	SC								
	PO	Y173 [210]	Y280 [115]				40 [429]	160 [429]	
Monoamine Oxidase Inhibition	IV								
	IP	0.75 [429]	2 [429]						
	IM								
	SC								
	PO								
Reserpine Antagonist	IV								
	IP	5 [455]							
	IM								
	SC								
	PO	15 [455]							
Barbiturate Sleep Potentiation	IV								
	IP								
	IM								
	SC	25 [142]							
	PO			50 [142]					
Behavioral	IV								
	IP								
	IM								
	SC		1.2 [456]						
	PO								
	IV								
	IP								
	IM								
	SC								
	PO								

ISONIAZID

(Armazide, INH, Rimifon)

mg/kg		Mouse	Rat	Guinea Pig	Rabbit	Cat	Dog	Monkey	
Lethal Dose Y–LD_{50} Z–MLD	IV	Y153 [428]			Y94 [428]		100 [428]		
	IP	Y132 [428]							
	IM	Y140 [428]							
	SC	Y160 [428]							
	PO	Y142 [428]	Y650 [115]		250 [428]		100 [428]		
Cardiovascular	IV					8 [428]			
	IP								
	IM								
	SC								
	PO								
	IV								
	IP								
	IM								
	SC								
	PO								
	IV								
	IP								
	IM								
	SC								
	PO								

IN VITRO

mg %	Cardiac	Vascular	Gut	Uterine	Visceral	Skeletal		

ISOPROTERENOL

(Aludrin, Isuprel, Norisodrine)

mg/kg		Mouse	Rat	Guinea Pig	Rabbit	Cat	Dog	Monkey	
Lethal Dose Y–LD_{50} Z–MLD	IV								
	IP	Y300 [111]							
	IM								
	SC								
	PO	Y450 [111]							
Cardiovascular	IV			0.01	0.002 [298]	0.005	0.005		
	IP								
	IM								
	SC								
	PO								
EEG (Desynchronization)	IV				0.005 [298]	0.005 [298]	0.005 [298]		
	IP								
	IM								
	SC								
	PO								
	IV								
	IP								
	IM								
	SC								
	PO								

IN VITRO

mg %	Cardiac	Vascular	Gut	Uterine	Visceral	Skeletal		
Langendorff	*0.001							
Guinea Pig						0.01		
Rabbit	0.025		0.01					

*Total mg

LEVALLORPHAN

(Lorfan, Naloxiphan, RO-1-7700)

mg/kg		Mouse	Rat	Guinea Pig	Rabbit	Cat	Dog	Monkey	
Lethal Dose Y–LD_{50} Z–MLD	IV								
	IP	Y184 210	Y185 210						
	IM								
	SC								
	PO		Y949 210						
Morphine Antagonist	IV						0.2		
	IP								
	IM								
	SC								
	PO								
EEG (Desynchronization)	IV				10 157	10 184			
	IP								
	IM								
	SC								
	PO								
Cardiovascular and Respiratory	IV				10 157				
	IP								
	IM								
	SC								
	PO								
	IV								
	IP								
	IM								
	SC								
	PO								
	IV								
	IP								
	IM								
	SC								
	PO								

LIDOCAINE

(Lignocaine, Xylocaine, Xylotox)

mg/kg		Mouse	Rat	Guinea Pig	Rabbit	Cat	Dog	Monkey	
Lethal Dose Y–LD_{50} Z–MLD	IV	Y31.5 [436]							
	IP								
	IM								
	SC	Y400 [437]							
	PO								
Anticonvulsant	IV					2.5 [440]		3 [442]	
	IP								
	IM								
	SC	4.9 [252]							
	PO								
Convulsant	IV				10 [438]	20 [440]			
	IP								
	IM								
	SC								
	PO								
EEG (Synchronization)	IV				5 [439]				
	IP								
	IM								
	SC								
	PO								
Block Afferent Nerve Discharge	IV						20 [441]		
	IP								
	IM								
	SC								
	PO								
	IV								
	IP								
	IM								
	SC								
	PO								

LYSERGIDE

(Delysid, LSD-25)

mg/kg		Mouse	Rat	Guinea Pig	Rabbit	Cat	Dog	Monkey	
Lethal Dose Y–LD$_{50}$ Z–MLD	IV	Y54 443			2 92				
	IP								
	IM								
	SC								
	PO								
Behavioral	IV				0.5 446	0.4	0.5 446	0.01 452	
	IP	4 369				0.02 447		0.1 185	
	IM	1 175				0.1 448		0.025 289	
	SC								
	PO								
Hyperthermic	IV				0.05 443				
	IP		4 444						
	IM								
	SC				0.06				
	PO								
EEG	IV				0.04	0.1 184	0.1 451		
	IP								
	IM								
	SC								
	PO								
Pentobarbital Antagonist	IV				0.14 159				
	IP					50 449			
	IM								
	SC								
	PO								
Metabolic Activity	IV					0.3 450			
	IP								
	IM								
	SC		0.625 445						
	PO								

mg/kg		Mouse	Rat	Guinea Pig	Rabbit	Cat	Dog	Monkey	
Antiseroton-ergic (B.P.)	IV		0.025 386			0.05 453			
	IP								
	IM								
	SC								
	PO								
Ataxic	IV								
	IP								
	IM							0.1 161	
	SC								
	PO								
Catatonic	IV								
	IP								
	IM							1.0 161	
	SC								
	PO								
	IV								
	IP								
	IM								
	SC								
	PO								

IN VITRO

mg %	Cardiac	Vascular	Gut	Uterine	Visceral	Skeletal		
Antiserotonergic				0.002 443				

MAGNESIUM SULFATE

(Epsom Salts)

mg/kg		Mouse	Rat	Guinea Pig	Rabbit	Cat	Dog	Monkey	
Lethal Dose Y–LD50 Z–MLD	IV	1100 [97]	1100 [97]	1100 [97]	1100 [97]	1100 [97]	750	1100 [97]	
	IP						1600 [109]		
	IM								
	SC			Z1800 [454]	Z1750 [454]	Z1000 [454]	1750 [109]		
	PO								
CNS Depressant	IV								
	IP								
	IM								
	SC								
	PO				1.3				
DFP Antagonist	IV								
	IP								
	IM				400				
	SC								
	PO								
	IV								
	IP								
	IM								
	SC								
	PO								

IN VITRO

mg %	Cardiac	Vascular	Gut	Uterine	Visceral	Skeletal		

MEBUTAMATE

(Capla)

mg/kg		Mouse	Rat	Guinea Pig	Rabbit	Cat	Dog	Monkey	
Lethal Dose Y–LD_{50} Z–MLD	IV								
	IP	Y460 457	Y410 457						
	IM								
	SC								
	PO	Y550 457	Y1160 457						
Cardiovascular	IV					30 467	20 457		
	IP				18 457				
	IM								
	SC								
	PO		120 457						
Anticonvulsant	IV								
	IP	90 457							
	IM								
	SC								
	PO								
	IV								
	IP								
	IM								
	SC								
	PO								

IN VITRO

mg %	Cardiac	Vascular	Gut	Uterine	Visceral	Skeletal		

MECAMYLAMINE

(Inversine, Mekamine, Revertina)

mg/kg		Mouse	Rat	Guinea Pig	Rabbit	Cat	Dog	Monkey	
Lethal Dose Y–LD$_{50}$ Z–MLD (as base)	IV	Y21 58							
	IP	Y39 58	Y54 58	Y52 58					
	IM								
	SC	Y93 58	Y145 58	Y127 58					
	PO	Y92 58	Y171 58	Y144 58			50 58		
Ganglionic Block (as base)	IV	2.5 58	2 386			0.23 113	1 58		
	IP	2.5 58							
	IM								
	SC								
	PO	2.5 58					2 58		
Cardiovascular	IV					7.5 459	1 458		
	IP								
	IM								
	SC								
	PO								
Neuromuscular Block	IV						10 214		
	IP								
	IM								
	SC								
	PO								
	IV								
	IP								
	IM								
	SC								
	PO								
	IV								
	IP								
	IM								
	SC								
	PO								

MEPENZOLATE

(Cantil)

mg/kg		Mouse	Rat	Guinea Pig	Rabbit	Cat	Dog	Monkey	
Lethal Dose $Y-LD_{50}$ $Z-MLD$	IV	Y9.8 460	Y21.8 460						
	IP								
	IM								
	SC								
	PO	Y900 460	Y1100 460						
Anticholinergic	IV					0.02 460	0.02 460		
	IP		5 460		0.015 460				
	IM								
	SC								
	PO								
	IV								
	IP								
	IM								
	SC								
	PO								
	IV								
	IP								
	IM								
	SC								
	PO								

IN VITRO

mg %	Cardiac	Vascular	Gut	Uterine	Visceral	Skeletal		
Anticholinergic			0.2 460					
Antihistaminic			200 460					

MEPHENESIN

(Myanesin, Tolseram, Tolserone)

mg/kg		Mouse	Rat	Guinea Pig	Rabbit	Cat	Dog	Monkey	
Lethal Dose Y–LD_{50} Z–MLD	IV								
	IP	Y471 [461]	283 [461]						
	IM								
	SC								
	PO	Y990 [461]	945 [461]						
Skeletal Muscle Relaxant (Central)	IV					20			
	IP	400 [204]	120						
	IM								
	SC						200		
	PO	550 [462]							
Strychnine Antagonist	IV								
	IP	100							
	IM		80						
	SC	200							
	PO								
Polysynaptic Reflex Inhibition	IV		50 [463]			20	25 [271]		
	IP								
	IM								
	SC								
	PO								
Righting Reflex Loss	IV						150		
	IP	130 [461]	103 [461]						
	IM								
	SC								
	PO	462 [461]	580 [461]						
	IV								
	IP								
	IM								
	SC								
	PO								

MEPHENTERMINE

(Mephine, Vialin, Wyamine)

mg/kg		Mouse	Rat	Guinea Pig	Rabbit	Cat	Dog	Monkey	
Lethal Dose Y–LD_{50} Z–MLD	IV								
	IP	Y110 464							
	IM								
	SC								
	PO								
Cardiovascular	IV					1 465	4 466		
	IP								
	IM								
	SC								
	PO								
Increased Coronary Blood Flow	IV						1 467		
	IP								
	IM								
	SC								
	PO								
	IV								
	IP								
	IM								
	SC								
	PO								

IN VITRO

mg %	Cardiac	Vascular	Gut	Uterine	Visceral	Skeletal		
Adrenolytic	0.1 468		1.0 465					

MEPHENYTOIN

(Mesantoin, Phenantoin, Sedantoinal)

mg/kg		Mouse	Rat	Guinea Pig	Rabbit	Cat	Dog	Monkey	
Lethal Dose Y–LD_{50} Z–MLD	IV								
	IP		270 475	Y215 352					
	IM								
	SC								
	PO	Y560 352			Y430 352	Y190 352			
Ataxic	IV								
	IP								
	IM								
	SC								
	PO	103 352			33 352	6.3 352			
	IV								
	IP								
	IM								
	SC								
	PO								
	IV								
	IP								
	IM								
	SC								
	PO								

IN VITRO

mg %	Cardiac	Vascular	Gut	Uterine	Visceral	Skeletal		

MEPROBAMATE

(Equanil, Miltown, Quaname)

mg/kg		Mouse	Rat	Guinea Pig	Rabbit	Cat	Dog	Monkey	
Lethal Dose Y–LD_{50} Z–MLD	IV	450 211							
	IP	Y710 461	410 461						
	IM								
	SC	550 17							
	PO	Y980 461	918 461						
Behavioral	IV					30 254			
	IP	100 469	135 470			20 145			
	IM	100 175							
	SC		300 231					400 211	
	PO		115 211		20 417	50 211	100 417	100 211	
Sedative	IV	200 211				45 462			
	IP	200 211	300 463						
	IM								
	SC	180 211							
	PO	100	150 117	100 472		65 557	30 557	325 473	
Spinal Cord Depressant	IV					50 813			
	IP								
	IM								
	SC								
	PO								
Cardiovascular	IV				25 471				
	IP								
	IM								
	SC								
	PO								
Hypnotic	IV	270 211							
	IP	260 211							
	IM								
	SC	300 211							
	PO	348 211	659 471						

mg/kg		Mouse	Rat	Guinea Pig	Rabbit	Cat	Dog	Monkey	
Anticonvulsant	IV								
	IP	155 461			100 474	20 110			
	IM								
	SC								
	PO	200 474							
Barbiturate Sleep Potentiation	IV								
	IP	80 469							
	IM								
	SC				100 142				
	PO		200 200	100 142					
Paralytic	IV	200 211							
	IP	200 211	300 463						
	IM								
	SC	180 211							
	PO	302 119	382 119						
	IV								
	IP								
	IM								
	SC								
	PO								

IN VITRO

mg %	Cardiac	Vascular	Gut	Uterine	Visceral	Skeletal		

MESCALINE

(Mezcaline)

mg/kg		Mouse	Rat	Guinea Pig	Rabbit	Cat	Dog	Monkey	
Lethal Dose Y–LD_{50} Z–MLD	IV								
	IP	Y500 115							
	IM								
	SC								
	PO								
CNS	IV				1.1 159		20 478		
	IP								
	IM								
	SC	30 119				50 476			
	PO								
Cardiovascular Respiratory	IV				25 157	7.5 477	5 478		
	IP								
	IM								
	SC								
	PO								
Behavioral	IV					1 110			
	IP								
	IM	50 251					70 479		
	SC								
	PO								
Decreased Spontaneous Motor Activity	IV								
	IP	50 813							
	IM								
	SC								
	PO								
	IV								
	IP								
	IM								
	SC								
	PO								

METARAMINOL

(Aramine, Pressonex)

mg/kg		Mouse	Rat	Guinea Pig	Rabbit	Cat	Dog	Monkey	
Lethal Dose	IV	Y51 [58]							
Y–LD_{50} Z–MLD	IP		Y41						
(as base)	IM								
	SC	Y92 [58]	Y117 [58]						
	PO	Y99 [58]	Y240						
Cardiovascular	IV						0.07 [58]		
(as base)	IP								
	IM								
	SC								
	PO								
Catechol Amine Depletion	IV						0.25 [58]		
	IP	0.1 [58]		0.2 [58]					
(Heart)	IM								
	SC								
	PO								
	IV								
	IP								
	IM								
	SC								
	PO								

IN VITRO

mg %	Cardiac	Vascular	Gut	Uterine	Visceral	Skeletal		

METHACHOLINE

(Acetyl-β-methylcholine, Mecholyl)

mg/kg		Mouse	Rat	Guinea Pig	Rabbit	Cat	Dog	Monkey	
Lethal Dose Y–LD_{50} Z–MLD	IV	Y15 [14]	Y20 [14]						
	IP								
	IM								
	SC	Y90 [14]	Y75 [14]						
	PO	Y1100 [14]	Y750 [14]						
Cholinergic	IV				0.002 [14]		0.002	7 [4]	
	IP					0.15 [4]		10 [4]	
	IM				5	0.15 [4]		10 [4]	
	SC				0.2 [14]	0.15 [4]		10 [4]	
	PO				50 [14]				
Cathartic	IV								
	IP								
	IM								
	SC						0.05 [14]		
	PO						25 [14]		
	IV								
	IP								
	IM								
	SC								
	PO								

IN VITRO

mg %	Cardiac	Vascular	Gut	Uterine	Visceral	Skeletal		

METHADONE

(Dolophine, Polamidon, Physeptone)

mg/kg		Mouse	Rat	Guinea Pig	Rabbit	Cat	Dog	Monkey	
Lethal Dose Y–LD_{50} Z–MLD	IV	Y17 [480]	Y10 [481]				26		
	IP	Y38 [480]	Y23 [480]						
	IM								
	SC	Y33 [480]	Y12 [480]	Y54 [480]			52	Y15 [480]	
	PO	Y93.7 [480]	Y95						
Analgetic	IV								
	IP	5	20						
	IM								
	SC	20	13 [482]	10			4		
	PO						1.1 [24]		
Cardiovascular Respiratory	IV				3 [43]		5		
	IP								
	IM								
	SC								
	PO								
Behavioral	IV								
	IP	2.5 [251]	10 [483]						
	IM								
	SC								
	PO								
	IV								
	IP								
	IM								
	SC								
	PO								
	IV								
	IP								
	IM								
	SC								
	PO								

METHAMPHETAMINE

(Desoxyn, Methedrine, Pervitin)

mg/kg		Mouse	Rat	Guinea Pig	Rabbit	Cat	Dog	Monkey	
Lethal Dose Y–LD_{50} Z–MLD	IV	Y10 [111]							
	IP	Y15 [111]	25 [485]						
	IM								
	SC	180				50			
	PO		4 [335]						
Increased Motor Activity	IV	0.5 [149]	1 [149]						
	IP	2 [149]	2 [149]						
	IM	1 [175]							
	SC	5 [484]	0.3 [200]			2 [149]			
	PO	2 [149]	2 [149]			2 [149]			
Behavioral	IV								
	IP	20 [177]				5 [487]			
	IM								
	SC		3.2 [486]						
	PO						1 [149]		
Analgetic	IV							0.5 [248]	
	IP								
	IM								
	SC								
	PO								
Analeptic	IV				2 [111]				
	IP								
	IM								
	SC								
	PO								
	IV								
	IP								
	IM								
	SC								
	PO								

METHARBITAL

(Gemonil)

mg/kg		Mouse	Rat	Guinea Pig	Rabbit	Cat	Dog	Monkey	
Lethal Dose Y–LD_{50} Z–MLD	IV								
	IP	Y500 111							
	IM								
	SC								
	PO	Y500 111							
Anticonvulsant	IV				20 111				
	IP								
	IM								
	SC								
	PO	25 111			50 111		50 111		
Ataxic	IV								
	IP	150 111							
	IM								
	SC								
	PO	200 111							
	IV								
	IP								
	IM								
	SC								
	PO								

IN VITRO

mg %	Cardiac	Vascular	Gut	Uterine	Visceral	Skeletal		

METHOXAMINE

(Pressomin, Vasoxyl, Vasylox)

mg/kg		Mouse	Rat	Guinea Pig	Rabbit	Cat	Dog	Monkey	
Lethal Dose Y−LD_{50} Z−MLD	IV	15 [149]							
	IP	Y92 [488]							
	IM								
	SC								
	PO	135 [149]							
Cardiovascular	IV					0.2 [489]	0.1 [490]		
	IP								
	IM						3 [149]		
	SC						0.8 [149]		
	PO						35 [149]		
Barbiturate Sleep Potentiation	IV								
	IP								
	IM								
	SC	8 [98]							
	PO								
	IV								
	IP								
	IM								
	SC								
	PO								

IN VITRO

mg %	Cardiac	Vascular	Gut	Uterine	Visceral	Skeletal		
Guinea Pig	0.5 [149]			*0.05 [149]				
Rabbit			*0.05 [149]	*0.05 [149]				

*mM

METHSCOPOLAMINE

(Pamine, Mescopildiopal, Proscomide)

mg/kg		Mouse	Rat	Guinea Pig	Rabbit	Cat	Dog	Monkey	
Lethal Dose Y–LD_{50} Z–MLD	IV								
	IP								
	IM								
	SC								
	PO								
Anticholinergic (Antisecretory)	IV		0.002 [491]						
	IP								
	IM				0.025 [491]		0.01 [491]		
	SC		0.2 [491]						
	PO		14 [491]				1.5 [491]		
Neuromuscular Block	IV						25 [491]		
	IP								
	IM								
	SC								
	PO								
Ganglionic Block	IV					5 [491]			
	IP								
	IM								
	SC								
	PO								
CNS (Stimulant)	IV								
	IP								
	IM								
	SC		5 [491]						
	PO		50 [491]						
	IV								
	IP								
	IM								
	SC								
	PO								

α-METHYLDOPA

(Aldomet)

mg/kg		Mouse	Rat	Guinea Pig	Rabbit	Cat	Dog	Monkey	
Lethal Dose Y–LD_{50} Z–MLD	IV	Y1900 [58]							
	IP	Y406 [58]	Y647 [58]						
	IM								
	SC								
	PO	Y5300 [58]	Y7490 [58]		Y713 [58]				
Decarboxylase Inhibition	IV		20 [493]	100 [494]		100 [493]			
	IP								
	IM								
	SC	100 [492]							
	PO								
Decreased Serotonin (Brain)	IV								
	IP								
	IM								
	SC	400 [492]		400 [492]					
	PO								
Catechol Amine Depletion (Heart)	IV	50 [58]					100 [58]		
	IP								
	IM								
	SC								
	PO								
Barbiturate Sleep Potentiation	IV								
	IP								
	IM								
	SC	100 [492]							
	PO								
	IV								
	IP								
	IM								
	SC								
	PO								

METHYLERGONOVINE

(Basofortina, Methergine, Partigin)

mg/kg		Mouse	Rat	Guinea Pig	Rabbit	Cat	Dog	Monkey	
Lethal Dose Y–LD_{50} Z–MLD	IV	Y85 352	Y23 352		Y2.6 352				
	IP								
	IM								
	SC								
	PO	Y187 352	Y93 352						
Oxytocic	IV				0.2 352	0.125 352			
	IP								
	IM								
	SC								
	PO								
	IV								
	IP								
	IM								
	SC								
	PO								
	IV								
	IP								
	IM								
	SC								
	PO								

IN VITRO

mg %	Cardiac	Vascular	Gut	Uterine	Visceral	Skeletal		

METHYLPHENIDATE

(Phenidylate, Ritalin)

mg/kg		Mouse	Rat	Guinea Pig	Rabbit	Cat	Dog	Monkey	
Lethal Dose	IV		Y48 [115]						
Y-LD$_{50}$	IP	Y450 [174]							
Z-MLD	IM								
	SC								
	PO		Y367 [115]						
CNS (Stimulant)	IV				5 [495]		2 [93]		
	IP	30 [174]							
	IM								
	SC	10 [93]	3.19 [85]					10 [89]	
	PO						10 [93]		
Antagonize Amphetamine Hypertension	IV					10 [497]	20 [497]		
	IP								
	IM								
	SC								
	PO								
Phentolamine Antagonist	IV						15 [498]		
	IP								
	IM								
	SC								
	PO								
Cardiovascular	IV		5 [157]		5 [495]	5 [496]	5 [496]		
	IP								
	IM								
	SC								
	PO								
	IV								
	IP								
	IM								
	SC								
	PO								

MORPHINE

mg/kg		Mouse	Rat	Guinea Pig	Rabbit	Cat	Dog	Monkey	
Lethal Dose Y−LD_{50} Z−MLD	IV	275 [307]	Y237 [481]						
	IP	Y500	920 [500]		Y500 [500]				
	IM			Z400 [502]					
	SC	Y531 [499]	Y572 [501]	Y391 [480]	Y600 [109]	Z60	210 [109]		
	PO		Y905 [481]	Z1000 [502]					
Analgetic Preanesthetic	IV		20 [503]				4	0.5 [248]	
	IP	2.3 [309]	5	12.1 [22]	5				
	IM		10					0.5 [248]	
	SC	7.0 [267]	1.6 [267]		15		4		
	PO	52.5 [267]	15.4 [267]						
Behavioral	IV								
	IP		10.25 [505]						
	IM								
	SC	50 [504]	1.3 [506]			1 [507]	5 [479]		
	PO	25.4 [701]							
Cardiovascular	IV		0.33 [507]			1	4		
	IP								
	IM								
	SC				2 [508]				
	PO								
Catatonic	IV							20 [506]	
	IP								
	IM								
	SC	40	125						
	PO		500 [269]						
EEG	IV		35		2 [337]	3 [509]	20 [509]		
	IP								
	IM								
	SC								
	PO								

mg/kg		Mouse	Rat	Guinea Pig	Rabbit	Cat	Dog	Monkey	
Convulsant	IV								
	IP								
	IM								
	SC				500	20			
	PO								
Polysynaptic Reflex Inhibition	IV					7 [510]			
	IP								
	IM								
	SC								
	PO								
	IV								
	IP								
	IM								
	SC								
	PO								
	IV								
	IP								
	IM								
	SC								
	PO								

IN VITRO

mg %	Cardiac	Vascular	Gut	Uterine	Visceral	Skeletal		
Rabbit	1		5					

MUSCARINE

mg/kg		Mouse	Rat	Guinea Pig	Rabbit	Cat	Dog	Monkey	
Lethal Dose Y−LD_{50} Z−MLD	IV	Y0.23 16							
	IP								
	IM								
	SC				30 511	2.8 109			
	PO	750			268 511	28.6 109			
Spasmogenic	IV			0.002 16	0.01 16	0.005 16	0.0005 16		
	IP								
	IM								
	SC								
	PO								
Cardiovascular	IV			0.005 16	0.005 16	0.001 16	0.0005 16		
	IP								
	IM								
	SC								
	PO								
	IV								
	IP								
	IM								
	SC								
	PO								

IN VITRO

mg %	Cardiac	Vascular	Gut	Uterine	Visceral	Skeletal		
Guinea Pig	0.002 16		0.002 16	0.01 16	0.002 16			
Rabbit	0.003 16		0.003 16	0.05 16	0.008 16			
Dog			0.0008 16	0.01 16	0.0003 16			

NALORPHINE

(Allorphine, Lethidrone, Nalline)

mg/kg		Mouse	Rat	Guinea Pig	Rabbit	Cat	Dog	Monkey	
Lethal Dose Y–LD_{50} Z–MLD	IV	Y190 58							
	IP	Y590 17							
	IM								
	SC	Y670 58							
	PO								
Morphine Antagonist (10 times Morphine Dose)	IV				5 513	3 514	2		
	IP	5 512	5						
	IM						0.4 97		
	SC		2 58				15		
	PO								
Analgetic	IV								
	IP	13.8 17	1.55 513						
	IM								
	SC	100 515							
	PO								
EEG	IV				0.004 516				
	IP								
	IM								
	SC								
	PO								
Antidepressant	IV								
	IP								
	IM								
	SC			10 90					
	PO								
	IV								
	IP								
	IM								
	SC								
	PO								

NEOSTIGMINE

(Kirkstigmine, Prostigmin, Vagostigmin)

mg/kg		Mouse	Rat	Guinea Pig	Rabbit	Cat	Dog	Monkey	
Lethal Dose Y−LD_{50} Z−MLD	IV	Y0.36 517	Y0.16 518		0.25 519		20 521		
	IP								
	IM				Y0.31 517				
	SC	Y0.8 517	Y0.37 518		Z12.5 520		Z13.5 520		
	PO	Y14.4 517							
Cholinergic	IV						0.025		
	IP								
	IM								
	SC						0.025		
	PO								
Anticurare	IV				0.25	0.025	0.17		
	IP								
	IM								
	SC		0.3						
	PO								
	IV								
	IP								
	IM								
	SC								
	PO								

IN VITRO

mg %	Cardiac	Vascular	Gut	Uterine	Visceral	Skeletal		
Rabbit		0.25	0.25					

NIALAMIDE

(Niamid, P-1133)

mg/kg		Mouse	Rat	Guinea Pig	Rabbit	Cat	Dog	Monkey	
Lethal Dose Y–LD_{50} Z–MLD	IV								
	IP	Y742 115							
	IM								
	SC								
	PO	Y1000 115	Y1700 115						
Monoamine-oxidase Inhibition (Brain)	IV				100 522				
	IP								
	IM								
	SC		30 173			10 173			
	PO								
Behavioral	IV								
	IP								
	IM								
	SC					10 173			
	PO								
Anticonvulsant	IV								
	IP	100 523	100 523						
	IM								
	SC								
	PO								
EEG (Synchronization)	IV								
	IP								
	IM								
	SC					10 173			
	PO								
	IV								
	IP								
	IM								
	SC								
	PO								

NICOTINE

mg/kg		Mouse	Rat	Guinea Pig	Rabbit	Cat	Dog	Monkey	
Lethal Dose $Y-LD_{50}$ $Z-MLD$	IV	Y7.1 [524]	Z1	Z4.5 [527]	Y9.4 [524]		Y5 [524]		
	IP	10							
	IM								
	SC	Z16 [525]	Y33.5 [526]	Z27.5 [528]	20 [528]				
	PO	Z24 [525]	Y55						
Behavioral	IV	0.3 [529]	0.23 [530]		0.02 [533]	0.02 [533]			
	IP	5 [369]	5.0 [531]						
	IM								
	SC		0.5 [532]				0.2 [534]		
	PO								
Cardiovascular	IV			0.3	0.1 [535]	0.2 [101]	0.25		
	IP								
	IM								
	SC						0.1		
	PO								
	IV								
	IP								
	IM								
	SC								
	PO								

IN VITRO

mg %	Cardiac	Vascular	Gut	Uterine	Visceral	Skeletal		
Rabbit	0.1		0.25					

NIKETHAMIDE

(Anacardone, Coramine, Tonocard)

mg/kg		Mouse	Rat	Guinea Pig	Rabbit	Cat	Dog	Monkey	
Lethal Dose $Y-LD_{50}$ $Z-MLD$	IV		Y191 [93]		250 [5]		175 [537]		
	IP	Y174 [284]	Y300 [537]	250 [537]	Y225 [537]				
	IM						175 [537]		
	SC	295 [536]	Y470 [538]	300 [537]	350 [537]				
	PO				650 [537]				
Analeptic	IV				10		75		
	IP								
	IM						75		
	SC						75		
	PO								
Behavioral CNS	IV				45 [157]		33 [24]		
	IP								
	IM	100 [175]							
	SC						33 [24]		
	PO								
Convulsant	IV								
	IP	145 [284]							
	IM								
	SC	201 [284]							
	PO								
Antiseroton-ergic	IV			10 [92]					
	IP								
	IM								
	SC								
	PO								
	IV								
	IP								
	IM								
	SC								
	PO								

NITROGLYCEROL

(Glyceryl Trinitrate, Perglottal, Trinitroglycerol)

mg/kg		Mouse	Rat	Guinea Pig	Rabbit	Cat	Dog	Monkey	
Lethal Dose Y–LD50 Z–MLD	IV				Z45 346				
	IP								
	IM		Z275 346		Z450 346				
	SC				500 346	200 346			
	PO		Z100						
Cardiovascular	IV						0.05		
	IP								
	IM								
	SC						0.01		
	PO		20 539						
	IV								
	IP								
	IM								
	SC								
	PO								
	IV								
	IP								
	IM								
	SC								
	PO								

IN VITRO

mg %	Cardiac	Vascular	Gut	Uterine	Visceral	Skeletal		

OUABAIN

(Astrobain, Gratibain, G-Strophanthin)

mg/kg		Mouse	Rat	Guinea Pig	Rabbit	Cat	Dog	Monkey	
Lethal Dose Y–LD_{50} Z–MLD	IV		17.2 540		0.2 303	Y0.11	0.12 542		
	IP	Y20							
	IM			Y0.26 541					
	SC	10 303	Y97 166	0.2 303	0.25 303	0.17 303	0.13 303		
	PO				14 303	2.4 109	1.5 109		
Cardiac	IV			0.02	0.05		0.025		
	IP								
	IM						0.025 97		
	SC								
	PO								
Arrhythmic	IV						0.05		
	IP								
	IM								
	SC								
	PO								
	IV								
	IP								
	IM								
	SC								
	PO								

IN VITRO

mg %	Cardiac	Vascular	Gut	Uterine	Visceral	Skeletal		
Rabbit	0.063		0.05					

PAPAVERINE

(Cardoverina, Dispamil)

mg/kg		Mouse	Rat	Guinea Pig	Rabbit	Cat	Dog	Monkey	
Lethal Dose Y–LD_{50} Z–MLD	IV	Y33.1 [543]							
	IP	Y750	Y63 [546]						
	IM								
	SC	Z500 [544]			Z250 [109]				
	PO	Y2500 [545]	Y745 [543]						
Cardiovascular	IV			10			7		
	IP								
	IM								
	SC								
	PO								
Catatonic	IV								
	IP								
	IM								
	SC					30 [476]			
	PO								
	IV								
	IP								
	IM								
	SC								
	PO								

IN VITRO

mg %	Cardiac	Vascular	Gut	Uterine	Visceral	Skeletal		
Guinea Pig			0.001					
Rabbit	5		7.5					
Antiserotonergic			0.3 [92]					

PARALDEHYDE

(Paracetaldehyde)

mg/kg		Mouse	Rat	Guinea Pig	Rabbit	Cat	Dog	Monkey	
Lethal Dose Y–LD_{50} Z–MLD	IV				Y450 7	Y450 7	Y500 7		
	IP	Z1500 547		Y1230 549					
	IM								
	SC	Z1650 547							
	PO	Y1650 548			5000 109		Y3500 109		
Anesthetic	IV				300 7	300 7	300 7		
	IP								
	IM								
	SC								
	PO				1000		2000		
Anticonvulsant	IV								
	IP								
	IM								
	SC								
	PO	1000 550							
	IV								
	IP								
	IM								
	SC								
	PO								

IN VITRO

mg %	Cardiac	Vascular	Gut	Uterine	Visceral	Skeletal		

PARGYLINE

(A-19120, Eutonyl, MO-911)

mg/kg		Mouse	Rat	Guinea Pig	Rabbit	Cat	Dog	Monkey	
Lethal Dose Y–LD_{50} Z–MLD	IV								
	IP	Y370 [551]	Y142 [551]			Y200 [551]		Y150 [551]	
	IM								
	SC								
	PO	Y680 [551]	Y300 [551]				Y175 [551]		
Monoamine-oxidase Inhibition	IV				10 [552]				
	IP	10 [69]							
	IM								
	SC								
	PO	75 [69]							
Increased Tissue Norepinephrine	IV				25 [552]				
	IP	100 [551]	50 [553]			100 [553]			
	IM								
	SC								
	PO								
Reverse Reserpine Depression (with DOPA)	IV				50 [69]				
	IP								
	IM								
	SC								
	PO							50 [551]	
Behavioral (irritability)	IV								
	IP								
	IM								
	SC								
	PO						100 [554]		
	IV								
	IP								
	IM								
	SC								
	PO								

PENTETRAZOL

(Cardiazol, Leptazol, Metrazol)

mg/kg		Mouse	Rat	Guinea Pig	Rabbit	Cat	Dog	Monkey	
Lethal Dose Y–LD_{50} Z–MLD	IV	40 176	50 569		Z70 572	80 570	40		
	IP	Y92 569	75 570	90 570					
	IM								
	SC	82.5 570	Y100 571	85 570	87.5 570	75 570			
	PO	97 284	170 570						
Convulsant	IV	48 121	20 573		20	11	20 134		
	IP	40.5 284	64 121	75					
	IM	40 251	100					64 575	
	SC	85							
	PO	68 284	175 574						
Analeptic	IV				60		20		
	IP		57.5 571						
	IM						10		
	SC	19 284					10		
	PO								
Cardiovascular	IV				15 157		50 410		
	IP								
	IM								
	SC								
	PO								
Decreased Motor Activity	IV								
	IP								
	IM	50 175							
	SC								
	PO								
	IV								
	IP								
	IM								
	SC								
	PO								

PENTOBARBITAL

(Embutal, Mebubarbital, Nembutal)

mg/kg		Mouse	Rat	Guinea Pig	Rabbit	Cat	Dog	Monkey	
Lethal Dose Y–LD_{50} Z–MLD	IV	Y80 [555]	Z50		Y45 [394]		62 [111]		
	IP	Y130 [555]	Y75	Y50 [556]	Z65 [129]	Z60 [449]	Z50		
	IM	Y124 [555]							
	SC		125 [66]						
	PO	Y280 [555]	Y118		Y275 [394]	Y100 [558]			
Anesthetic	IV	35 [111]	25 [111]	30 [111]	30 [111]	25 [111]	30 [111]	25 [111]	
	IP	60 [111]	50 [111]	35 [111]	40 [111]	38 [111]	38 [111]	30 [111]	
	IM					15 [557]			
	SC						30 [111]		
	PO	80 [111]	50 [111]	50 [111]	45 [111]	50 [111]	50 [111]	45 [111]	
Behavioral	IV				5 [562]	3.4 [563]		12 [564]	
	IP		10 [470]					15 [185]	
	IM							20 [289]	
	SC		20 [231]						
	PO	35 [561]	5 [232]						
EEG (Synchroni- zation	IV				10 [559]	5	10 [560]		
	IP								
	IM								
	SC								
	PO						40 [560]		
Cardiovascular	IV					6 [565]	10 [560]		
	IP								
	IM								
	SC								
	PO								
Neuronal Membrane Stabilization	IV					10 [566]			
	IP								
	IM								
	SC								
	PO								

mg/kg		Mouse	Rat	Guinea Pig	Rabbit	Cat	Dog	Monkey	
Ataxic	IV	12.9 566			15 562				
	IP								
	IM								
	SC		5 567						
	PO								
Tremor	IV								
	IP					30 568			
	IM								
	SC								
	PO								
Increased Serotonin (Brain)	IV								
	IP		50 31						
	IM								
	SC								
	PO								
Muscle Contraction (Denervated)	IV							25	
	IP								
	IM								
	SC								
	PO								
	IV								
	IP								
	IM								
	SC								
	PO								
	IV								
	IP								
	IM								
	SC								
	PO								

PENTOLINIUM

(Ansolysen, Pentilium)

mg/kg		Mouse	Rat	Guinea Pig	Rabbit	Cat	Dog	Monkey	
Lethal Dose Y–LD50 Z–MLD	IV	Y29 214							
	IP	Y36 214							
	IM								
	SC								
	PO	Y512 214							
Ganglionic Block	IV					0.07 113	0.5		
	IP		5 381						
	IM								
	SC								
	PO								
Epinephrine Sensitization	IV					0.24 154			
	IP								
	IM								
	SC								
	PO								
Neuromuscular Block	IV						10 214		
	IP								
	IM								
	SC								
	PO								
	IV								
	IP								
	IM								
	SC								
	PO								
	IV								
	IP								
	IM								
	SC								
	PO								

PERPHENAZINE

(Fentazin, PZC, Trilafon)

mg/kg		Mouse	Rat	Guinea Pig	Rabbit	Cat	Dog	Monkey	
Lethal Dose $Y-LD_{50}$ Z-MLD	IV	37 [228]	38 [228]			35 [417]	51 [228]		
	IP		124 [228]						
	IM								
	SC								
	PO	120 [228]	318 [228]				100 [228]		
"Tranquilize" (free base)	IV								
	IP								
	IM						0.5 [228]	0.2 [576]	
	SC	0.1 [223]	0.1 [223]			0.1 [223]	0.1 [223]	0.1 [223]	
	PO	1.0 [223]	1.0 [223]			1.0 [223]	1.0 [223]	1.5 [223]	
Behavioral	IV								
	IP		0.25 [577]			4 [417]			
	IM								
	SC		0.4 [578]						
	PO	10 [417]	2 [417]			10 [417]	10 [417]		
Preanesthetic Medication	IV					0.55 [97]	0.55 [97]		
	IP								
	IM					0.55 [97]	0.55 [97]		
	SC								
	PO		10 [417]			0.88 [97]	0.88 [97]		
Adrenolytic	IV					1 [417]	1 [417]		
	IP								
	IM								
	SC								
	PO								
Cardiovascular	IV				1 [471]	2 [417]	2 [417]		
	IP								
	IM								
	SC								
	PO								

mg/kg		Mouse	Rat	Guinea Pig	Rabbit	Cat	Dog	Monkey	
EEG	IV				3 417				
	IP								
	IM								
	SC								
	PO								
Experimental Shock Protection	IV						1 228		
	IP								
	IM		1.5 228						
	SC								
	PO								
Ataxic	IV						2 417		
	IP								
	IM								
	SC								
	PO								
	IV								
	IP								
	IM								
	SC								
	PO								

IN VITRO

mg %	Cardiac	Vascular	Gut	Uterine	Visceral	Skeletal		

PETHIDINE

(Dolantin, Dolosal, Meperidine)

mg/kg		Mouse	Rat	Guinea Pig	Rabbit	Cat	Dog	Monkey	
Lethal Dose Y–LD_{50} Z–MLD	IV	Y50 [579]	Y34 [580]		Y30 [579]		100		
	IP	Y150	Y93 [580]						
	IM								
	SC	Y195 [579]	Y200 [579]						
	PO	Y178 [579]	Y170		Y500 [579]				
Analgetic Sedative	IV		10 [269]		10 [191]		2		
	IP	40	50 [580]	51.8 [22]					
	IM					7.5	10		
	SC	60	43.6 [581]				25		
	PO		150 [580]			11 [24]	11 [24]		
Spinal Reflex Depressant	IV					13 [510]			
	IP								
	IM								
	SC		100 [269]						
	PO								
	IV								
	IP								
	IM								
	SC								
	PO								

IN VITRO

mg %	Cardiac	Vascular	Gut	Uterine	Visceral	Skeletal		
Rabbit	20		20					

PHENACEMIDE

(Carbanmide, Phenurone, Epiclase)

mg/kg		Mouse	Rat	Guinea Pig	Rabbit	Cat	Dog	Monkey	
Lethal Dose Y—LD_{50} Z—MLD	IV								
	IP								
	IM								
	SC								
	PO	Y5000 [111]			3500 [111]	2000 [111]	3500 [111]		
Anticonvulsant	IV								
	IP								
	IM								
	SC								
	PO	300 [111]			300 [111]		*1100 [97]		
Behavioral	IV								
	IP								
	IM								
	SC								
	PO	205							
Ataxic	IV								
	IP								
	IM								
	SC								
	PO	400 [111]							
	IV								
	IP								
	IM								
	SC								
	PO								
	IV								
	IP								
	IM								
	SC								
	PO								

*Total dose

PHENAZONE

(Analgesine, Anti-Pyrine, Pyrazolin)

mg/kg		Mouse	Rat	Guinea Pig	Rabbit	Cat	Dog	Monkey	
Lethal Dose Y–LD$_{50}$ Z–MLD	IV				700 [109]				
	IP	Z1000 [4]							
	IM	Z1000 [4]							
	SC	1000 [109]		1000 [109]	1250 [109]	700 [109]			
	PO	Y1800 [109]	Y1800 [18]	1400 [109]			750 [109]		
Analgetic Antipyretic	IV								
	IP				100 [4]	100 [4]			
	IM				100 [4]	100 [4]			
	SC		600 [21]		100 [4]	100 [4]			
	PO		220 [18]		500 [4]	500 [4]	*1000 [97]		
Anti-inflammatory	IV								
	IP								
	IM								
	SC								
	PO			100 [55]					
	IV								
	IP								
	IM								
	SC								
	PO								

*Total dose

IN VITRO

mg %	Cardiac	Vascular	Gut	Uterine	Visceral	Skeletal		

PHENELZINE

(Alazine, Nardelzine, Nardil)

mg/kg		Mouse	Rat	Guinea Pig	Rabbit	Cat	Dog	Monkey	
Lethal Dose Y–LD_{50} Z–MLD	IV	Y157 [115]							
	IP								
	IM								
	SC								
	PO	Y156 [115]	210 [455]						
Analgetic	IV								
	IP								
	IM								
	SC								
	PO	12 [582]							
Respiratory	IV								
	IP	10 [455]							
	IM								
	SC								
	PO	15 [455]							
Monoamine Oxidase Inhibition	IV	48 [608]							
	IP	32 [608]							
	IM								
	SC								
	PO								
Cardiovascular	IV					0.6 [608]	5 [583]		
	IP					15 [608]			
	IM								
	SC								
	PO								
	IV								
	IP								
	IM								
	SC								
	PO								

PHENIPRAZINE

(Catron, JB-516, Katroniazid)

mg/kg		Mouse	Rat	Guinea Pig	Rabbit	Cat	Dog	Monkey	
Lethal Dose Y–LD_{50} Z–MLD	IV	Y60.6 460	Y44.5 460			35 584			
	IP	Y122	50						
	IM								
	SC	Y95 460	Y45.3 460			35 584			
	PO	Y73 460	Y34.1 460						
Monoamine-oxidase Inhibition	IV	3 430			3 430	1.5	5 372		
	IP		20 584				15		
	IM								
	SC	3 430			2 430	1.5 91			
	PO								
CNS Behavioral	IV				5 584	25 584	10 586		
	IP	50 585	30 585				25 584		
	IM								
	SC		20 460		2 430	25 584			
	PO								
Cardiovascular	IV		10 218	5	5	5	5 372		
	IP								
	IM								
	SC								
	PO								
Barbiturate Sleep Potentiation	IV								
	IP	10 585	10 585						
	IM								
	SC								
	PO								
	IV								
	IP								
	IM								
	SC								
	PO								

PHENOBARBITAL

(Gardenal, Luminal, Sental)

mg/kg		Mouse	Rat	Guinea Pig	Rabbit	Cat	Dog	Monkey	
Lethal Dose Y–LD_{50} Z–MLD	IV				Y185 122				
	IP	Y340 122	Y190 122		Z150 588				
	IM				Z150 128				
	SC	Y230	Y200 68						
	PO	Y325 391	Y660 587		Z150 588	Y175 558			
Anesthetic	IV	134 65	100 589		200 590	*60 97	80 591		
	IP			100		180	150	100	
	IM					*60 97	30 557		
	SC	96					30 557		
	PO	107		30 76		*60 97	150	125	
Anticonvulsant	IV				25 594		25 594		
	IP	25 592	25 592					15 595	
	IM								
	SC	20	30 414		50				
	PO	25	25 593			*45 24	*150 24		
Behavioral	IV								
	IP		15 470						
	IM	40 175	30 230						
	SC		39 596						
	PO	90 505					75 597		
Cardiovascular	IV				50 598		20 599		
	IP								
	IM								
	SC								
	PO								
Ataxic	IV								
	IP								
	IM								
	SC		88 596						
	PO	250 484							

*Total dose

mg/kg		Mouse	Rat	Guinea Pig	Rabbit	Cat	Dog	Monkey	
Antidiuretic	IV						40 591		
	IP								
	IM								
	SC				120 591				
	PO								
Reflex Depressant	IV					10 564			
	IP								
	IM								
	SC								
	PO								
	IV								
	IP								
	IM								
	SC								
	PO								
	IV								
	IP								
	IM								
	SC								
	PO								

IN VITRO

mg %	Cardiac	Vascular	Gut	Uterine	Visceral	Skeletal		

PHENOXYBENZAMINE

(Dibenzyline)

mg/kg		Mouse	Rat	Guinea Pig	Rabbit	Cat	Dog	Monkey	
Lethal Dose $Y-LD_{50}$ Z-MLD	IV						Z10 [82]		
	IP								
	IM								
	SC								
	PO	Y1535 [82]	Y2500 [82]	Y500 [82]					
Adrenolytic	IV		0.031 [253]		15 [220]	3.0 [404]	15		
	IP		1 [383]						
	IM								
	SC								
	PO								
CNS	IV				1.5 [87]				
	IP	5 [350]							
	IM								
	SC		5 [350]						
	PO								
Catechol Amine Depletion	IV						20 [816]		
	IP		10 [600]						
	IM								
	SC								
	PO								
Decreased Blood Pressure in Experimental Hypertension	IV								
	IP		0.2 [387]						
	IM								
	SC								
	PO		50 [387]						
EEG (Synchronization)	IV				1.5 [298]				
	IP								
	IM								
	SC								
	PO								

mg/kg		Mouse	Rat	Guinea Pig	Rabbit	Cat	Dog	Monkey	
	IV								
	IP								
	IM								
	SC								
	PO								
	IV								
	IP								
	IM								
	SC								
	PO								
	IV								
	IP								
	IM								
	SC								
	PO								
	IV								
	IP								
	IM								
	SC								
	PO								

IN VITRO

mg %	Cardiac	Vascular	Gut	Uterine	Visceral	Skeletal		
Adrenolytic		0.005		0.005	0.006			

PHENTOLAMINE

(C-7337, Regitine, Rogitine)

mg/kg		Mouse	Rat	Guinea Pig	Rabbit	Cat	Dog	Monkey	
Lethal Dose Y–LD_{50} Z–MLD	IV		Y75 603						
	IP								
	IM								
	SC		Y275 603						
	PO	Y1000 119	Y1250 603						
Adrenolytic	IV		10 218		3 305	2 497	1 408		
	IP								
	IM								
	SC				1 603	1 603	1 603		
	PO								
CNS	IV								
	IP								
	IM								
	SC								
	PO	150 119							
	IV								
	IP								
	IM								
	SC								
	PO								

IN VITRO

mg %	Cardiac	Vascular	Gut	Uterine	Visceral	Skeletal		
Adrenolytic			0.01 604					
Antiserotonergic			0.1 92					

PHENYLBUTAZONE

(Butazolidin, Reudox, Ticinil)

mg/kg		Mouse	Rat	Guinea Pig	Rabbit	Cat	Dog	Monkey	
Lethal Dose Y–LD50 Z–MLD	IV	Y123 605							
	IP	Y336 17	Y215 605						
	IM								
	SC								
	PO								
Analgetic	IV				100 50				
	IP	150 50							
	IM								
	SC								
	PO								
Anti-inflammatory	IV								
	IP								
	IM								
	SC		200 50						
	PO		600 50	1800 55					
	IV								
	IP								
	IM								
	SC								
	PO								

IN VITRO

mg %	Cardiac	Vascular	Gut	Uterine	Visceral	Skeletal		

PHENYLEPHRINE

(Adrianol, Meta-Sympatol, Neo-Synephrine)

mg/kg		Mouse	Rat	Guinea Pig	Rabbit	Cat	Dog	Monkey	
Lethal Dose Y–LD_{50} Z–MLD	IV		6.8 [607]						
	IP	Y1000							
	IM								
	SC	1000 [606]	28 [607]						
	PO								
Cardiovascular	IV			0.04			0.03 [408]		
	IP								
	IM								
	SC								
	PO								
CNS (Stimulant)	IV								
	IP								
	IM								
	SC						0.5		
	PO								
	IV								
	IP								
	IM								
	SC								
	PO								

IN VITRO

mg %	Cardiac	Vascular	Gut	Uterine	Visceral	Skeletal		
Rabbit	0.04		0.01					

PHENYTOIN

(Dilantin, Diphenylhydantoin, Eptoin)

mg/kg		Mouse	Rat	Guinea Pig	Rabbit	Cat	Dog	Monkey	
Lethal Dose Y–LD_{50} Z–MLD	IV		Z160 [610]		Y125 [70]		Z90 [610]		
	IP	Y200 [609]	Y280 [70]						
	IM								
	SC								
	PO	Y490 [226]	Z > 2200 [610]						
Anticonvulsant	IV					30 [613]			
	IP	20 [611]	135 [612]		60				
	IM								
	SC	75	300		55				
	PO	50	2200 [610]				*50 [24]		
Toxic Dose (Emesis)	IV						5		
	IP	800	200						
	IM								
	SC								
	PO	84 [226]							
Tremorine Antagonist	IV								
	IP								
	IM	99 [140]							
	SC								
	PO								
Behavioral	IV								
	IP								
	IM		50 [230]						
	SC								
	PO								
Cardiovascular	IV				30 [818]		5 [818]		
	IP								
	IM								
	SC								
	PO								

*Total dose

PHENYTOIN (continued)

mg/kg		Mouse	Rat	Guinea Pig	Rabbit	Cat	Dog	Monkey	
Vagus Nerve Depression	IV						20 818		
	IP								
	IM								
	SC								
	PO								
Respiratory Depression	IV				30 818		20 818		
	IP								
	IM								
	SC								
	PO								
Uterin Activity Depression	IV				40 819		20 819		
	IP								
	IM								
	SC								
	PO								
	IV								
	IP								
	IM								
	SC								
	PO								

IN VITRO

mg %	Cardiac	Vascular	Gut	Uterine	Visceral	Skeletal		
Rabbit				0.1 819				

PHYSOSTIGMINE

(Eserine)

mg/kg		Mouse	Rat	Guinea Pig	Rabbit	Cat	Dog	Monkey	
Lethal Dose Y–LD_{50} Z–MLD	IV	0.5 [519]			0.4 [614]	0.25 [614]			
	IP								
	IM								
	SC	0.75			3 [519]				
	PO	Y3.0 [115]							
Cholinergic	IV						0.5		
	IP								
	IM								
	SC				1 [88]	*0.38	1		
	PO								
EEG (desynchronization)	IV				0.3 [60]	0.2			
	IP								
	IM								
	SC								
	PO								
Behavioral	IV						0.1		
	IP								
	IM								
	SC								
	PO								
Increased Spinal Cord Inhibition	IV					1.5 [379]			
	IP								
	IM								
	SC								
	PO								
Bulbocapnine Potentiation	IV				0.1 [288]				
	IP	0.05 [615]							
	IM								
	SC								
	PO								

*Total dose

PHYSOSTIGMINE (continued)

mg/kg		Mouse	Rat	Guinea Pig	Rabbit	Cat	Dog	Monkey	
Tremor	IV								
	IP	5 369							
	IM								
	SC								
	PO								
	IV								
	IP								
	IM								
	SC								
	PO								
	IV								
	IP								
	IM								
	SC								
	PO								
	IV								
	IP								
	IM								
	SC								
	PO								

IN VITRO

mg %	Cardiac	Vascular	Gut	Uterine	Visceral	Skeletal		
Rabbit	0.025		0.5					

PICROTOXIN

(Cocculin)

mg/kg		Mouse	Rat	Guinea Pig	Rabbit	Cat	Dog	Monkey	
Lethal Dose Y–LD_{50} Z–MLD	IV	Z4	Y3 166		Z1.25 617				
	IP	Y7.2 284	Y6.5 166						
	IM								
	SC	Y7.04 284	4.7 616	8 109	Z2.5 617		2.2 109		
	PO	Y14.8 284							
Analeptic	IV				3		0.3		
	IP	10 123				1.5 618	0.3		
	IM						0.3		
	SC	1.6 284					0.3		
	PO								
CNS (Stimulant)	IV	2.9 121	2.9 121		0.89 121		*2 24		
	IP		9 130						
	IM								
	SC	5.9 121	3 617						
	PO								
Convulsant	IV					0.3 134			
	IP	4.8 284							
	IM								
	SC	3.14 284							
	PO	8.43 284							
Behavioral	IV								
	IP								
	IM	1 175							
	SC								
	PO								
	IV								
	IP								
	IM								
	SC								
	PO								

*Total dose

PILOCARPINE

mg/kg		Mouse	Rat	Guinea Pig	Rabbit	Cat	Dog	Monkey	
Lethal Dose Y–LD_{50} Z–MLD	IV				175 [109]				
	IP	Y500							
	IM								
	SC								
	PO								
Cholinergic	IV						3		
	IP								
	IM					*2 [24]	*12 [24]		
	SC		160 [619]		5	*2 [24]	0.75		
	PO								
Anticonvulsant	IV								
	IP								
	IM								
	SC	160 [620]	26 [620]						
	PO								
	IV								
	IP								
	IM								
	SC								
	PO								

*Total dose

IN VITRO

mg %	Cardiac	Vascular	Gut	Uterine	Visceral	Skeletal		
Rabbit	0.5		1	1				

PIPRADOL

(Meratran, MRD-108, Piridol)

mg/kg		Mouse	Rat	Guinea Pig	Rabbit	Cat	Dog	Monkey	
Lethal Dose Y−LD_{50} Z−MLD	IV		Y30 115		Y15 117				
	IP	Y94 115							
	IM								
	SC	Y240 115	Y240 117						
	PO		Y180 115						
CNS Stimulant and Increased Motor Activity	IV		6 117						
	IP	10 323							
	IM								
	SC	20 204	2.74 85						
	PO								
Analeptic	IV				12.5 117		2 133		
	IP		20 621						
	IM								
	SC								
	PO								
Cardiovascular	IV					8 117			
	IP								
	IM								
	SC								
	PO								
Behavioral	IV								
	IP		5 622						
	IM								
	SC								
	PO								
	IV								
	IP								
	IM								
	SC								
	PO								

POTASSIUM CYANIDE

mg/kg		Mouse	Rat	Guinea Pig	Rabbit	Cat	Dog	Monkey	
Lethal Dose Y–LD_{50} Z–MLD	IV	2.5 109	Z2.5 195				5		
	IP	Z6 109							
	IM		8						
	SC	Y6.02 273	Z17 195						
	PO	Y16 623	Z12.5 195		Y5		1.6 624		
Vagal Bradycardia Potentiation	IV					0.03 625			
	IP								
	IM								
	SC								
	PO								
Increased O_2 Consumption	IV								
	IP								
	IM								
	SC		9.6 626						
	PO								
	IV								
	IP								
	IM								
	SC								
	PO								

IN VITRO

mg %	Cardiac	Vascular	Gut	Uterine	Visceral	Skeletal		

PROBARBITAL

(Ipral)

mg/kg		Mouse	Rat	Guinea Pig	Rabbit	Cat	Dog	Monkey	
Lethal Dose Y–LD_{50} Z–MLD	IV				140 [27]				
	IP	250 [66]	110 [66]		110 [66]				
	IM								
	SC		310 [66]						
	PO				160 [66]	140 [66]			
Anesthetic	IV								
	IP	75 [66]			66 [66]				
	IM								
	SC		225 [66]						
	PO								
	IV								
	IP								
	IM								
	SC								
	PO								
	IV								
	IP								
	IM								
	SC								
	PO								

IN VITRO

mg %	Cardiac	Vascular	Gut	Uterine	Visceral	Skeletal		

PROBENECID

(Benemid)

mg/kg		Mouse	Rat	Guinea Pig	Rabbit	Cat	Dog	Monkey	
Lethal Dose Y–LD_{50} Z–MLD	IV	Y458 627			Y304 627		Y270 627		
	IP		Y394 627						
	IM								
	SC	Y1156 627	Y611 627						
	PO	Y1666 627	Y1604 627						
Uricosuric	IV						16 58		
	IP								
	IM								
	SC								
	PO		300 58				30 58		
	IV								
	IP								
	IM								
	SC								
	PO								
	IV								
	IP								
	IM								
	SC								
	PO								

IN VITRO

mg %	Cardiac	Vascular	Gut	Uterine	Visceral	Skeletal		

PROCAINE

(Allocaine, Neocaine, Novocaine)

mg/kg		Mouse	Rat	Guinea Pig	Rabbit	Cat	Dog	Monkey	
Lethal Dose Y–LD_{50} Z–MLD	IV	Y45 111	Y50	Y51 629	Y57 249	Z45	Y62.4 7		
	IP	Y230 111	Y250 166	Z60					
	IM	Y630 628	Y1600 111						
	SC	Y800 259	Y2100 259	Z430	Z460	Z450	Z250		
	PO	Y500 111							
Convulsant	IV				30				
	IP								
	IM			100 630					
	SC						100		
	PO								
Block Afferent Nerve Discharge	IV					10 292	20 441		
	IP								
	IM								
	SC								
	PO								
Decreased Intestinal Motility and Pain	IV					10 440			
	IP								
	IM								
	SC								
	PO								
Cardiovascular	IV				20 631	20 631	20 631		
	IP								
	IM								
	SC								
	PO								
	IV								
	IP								
	IM								
	SC								
	PO								

PROCHLORPERAZINE

(Compazine, Novamin, Stemetil)

mg/kg		Mouse	Rat	Guinea Pig	Rabbit	Cat	Dog	Monkey	
Lethal Dose Y−LD_{50} Z−MLD	IV	57 [82]	20 [235]		5 [235]		Z 100 [82]		
	IP								
	IM								
	SC								
	PO	Y1220 [82]	Y1800 [82]				Z 102 [82]		
Behavioral	IV								
	IP		8 [227]						
	IM								
	SC	10 [561]	1.3 [95]						
	PO	7.4 [505]							
Cardiovascular	IV					0.1 [82]	0.5 [82]		
	IP								
	IM								
	SC								
	PO		0.05 [82]						
Decreased Activity	IV								
	IP								
	IM								
	SC	1 [578]							
	PO								
Catatonic	IV								
	IP		16.5 [227]						
	IM								
	SC								
	PO								
EEG (Synchronization)	IV								
	IP								
	IM				5				
	SC								
	PO								

mg/kg		Mouse	Rat	Guinea Pig	Rabbit	Cat	Dog	Monkey	
	IV								
	IP								
	IM								
	SC								
	PO								
	IV								
	IP								
	IM								
	SC								
	PO								
	IV								
	IP								
	IM								
	SC								
	PO								
	IV								
	IP								
	IM								
	SC								
	PO								

IN VITRO

mg %	Cardiac	Vascular	Gut	Uterine	Visceral	Skeletal		
Spasmolytic			0.1					
Anticholinergic			*0.8 235					
Antihistaminic		*0.11 235	*0.002 235					
Antiserotonergic			*0.0005 235					

*Total mg

PRODILIDIN

mg/kg		Mouse	Rat	Guinea Pig	Rabbit	Cat	Dog	Monkey	
Lethal Dose Y–LD_{50} Z–MLD	IV	Y91 [267]	Y74 [267]						
	IP								
	IM								
	SC	Y194 [267]	Y188 [267]						
	PO	Y318 [267]	Y253 [267]						
Analgetic	IV	30 [267]	11.2 [267]						
	IP								
	IM		26.3 [267]						
	SC	72.3 [267]	17.8 [267]						
	PO	84 [267]	17.3 [267]						
Emetic	IV								
	IP								
	IM						2.5 [267]		
	SC					60 [267]	10 [267]		
	PO					60 [267]	10 [267]		
Cardiovascular	IV					10 [267]	10 [267]		
	IP								
	IM								
	SC								
	PO								
Convulsant	IV								
	IP								
	IM								
	SC					80 [267]		60 [267]	
	PO								
	IV								
	IP								
	IM								
	SC								
	PO								

PROMAZINE

(Protactyl, Sparine, Verophen)

mg/kg		Mouse	Rat	Guinea Pig	Rabbit	Cat	Dog	Monkey	
Lethal Dose Y–LD_{50} Z–MLD	IV	Y38 [235]	Y29 [235]		Y21 [235]				
	IP								
	IM						Y4.4 [557]		
	SC								
	PO	Y485 [226]							
Sedative and EEG (Synchronization)	IV				2 [632]	3.3 [97]	1.5		
	IP								
	IM					3.3 [97]	5.5 [557]		
	SC								
	PO	40 [119]				3.3 [97]	9 [557]		
Behavioral	IV								
	IP	5 [633]	2.4 [227]						
	IM								
	SC								
	PO								
Adrenolytic	IV		0.041 [253]						
	IP	10 [634]							
	IM								
	SC								
	PO								
Analgetic	IV								
	IP	10 [238]	120 [238]						
	IM								
	SC								
	PO	100 [231]							
Flexor Reflex Depression	IV								
	IP				1 [238]				
	IM								
	SC								
	PO								

mg/kg		Mouse	Rat	Guinea Pig	Rabbit	Cat	Dog	Monkey	
Barbiturate Sleep Potentiation	IV						2 [425]		
	IP	14.4 [227]							
	IM								
	SC	5 [118]							
	PO								
Catatonic	IV								
	IP		3.3 [227]						
	IM								
	SC								
	PO								
	IV								
	IP								
	IM								
	SC								
	PO								
	IV								
	IP								
	IM								
	SC								
	PO								

IN VITRO

mg %	Cardiac	Vascular	Gut	Uterine	Visceral	Skeletal		
Anticholinergic			*0.175 [235]					
Antihistaminic		0.04 [235]	*0.004 [235]					
Antiserotonergic			*0.0006 [235]					
Anti-$BaCl_2$			*0.0002 [235]					

*Total mg

PROMETHAZINE

(Atosil, Phenergan, Thiergan)

mg/kg		Mouse	Rat	Guinea Pig	Rabbit	Cat	Dog	Monkey	
Lethal Dose Y–LD_{50} Z–MLD	IV	Y75 [235]	Y45 [235]	Y42.5 [629]	Y19 [235]				
	IP								
	IM								
	SC	Y750	Y225						
	PO	Y125 [88]							
Anticonvulsant	IV								
	IP	40							
	IM								
	SC	72 [252]							
	PO								
Barbiturate Sleep Potentiation	IV								
	IP								
	IM								
	SC	20 [88]	10 [88]				5 [88]		
	PO								
Sympatho-mimetic Sensitization	IV					15 [635]			
	IP	40 [251]							
	IM								
	SC								
	PO								

IN VITRO

mg %	Cardiac	Vascular	Gut	Uterine	Visceral	Skeletal		
Antihistaminic		0.006 [235]	0.01					
Anticholinergic			1 [88]					
Antiserotonergic			*0.0007 [235]					
Adrenolytic				0.1 [88]				

*Total mg

PROMETHAZINE (continued)

mg/kg		Mouse	Rat	Guinea Pig	Rabbit	Cat	Dog	Monkey	
Motion Sickness Antagonist	IV								
	IP								
	IM						*125 [97]		
	SC								
	PO								
	IV								
	IP								
	IM								
	SC								
	PO								
	IV								
	IP								
	IM								
	SC								
	PO								
	IV								
	IP								
	IM								
	SC								
	PO								

*Total dose

IN VITRO

mg %	Cardiac	Vascular	Gut	Uterine	Visceral	Skeletal		
Anti-$BaCl_2$			0.5 [88]					

PRONETHANOL

(Alderlin, Nethalide)

mg/kg		Mouse	Rat	Guinea Pig	Rabbit	Cat	Dog	Monkey	
Lethal Dose Y–LD_{50} Z–MLD	IV	Y50 [636]	Y50 [636]						
	IP								
	IM								
	SC								
	PO	Y900 [636]	Y900 [636]			300 [636]			
Adrenolytic (β-block)	IV					5 [636]	5 [636]		
	IP								
	IM								
	SC								
	PO						10 [636]		
	IV								
	IP								
	IM								
	SC								
	PO								
	IV								
	IP								
	IM								
	SC								
	PO								

IN VITRO

mg %	Cardiac	Vascular	Gut	Uterine	Visceral	Skeletal		
Adrenolytic	0.01		1 [636]					

PROPANTHELINE

(Neo-Metantyl, Pro-Banthine)

mg/kg		Mouse	Rat	Guinea Pig	Rabbit	Cat	Dog	Monkey	
Lethal Dose Y–LD50 Z–MLD	IV								
	IP								
	IM								
	SC								
	PO								
Anticholinergic	IV								
	IP		5 144						
	IM						5 638		
	SC		0.05 637						
	PO								
Ganglionic Block	IV					0.7 113			
	IP								
	IM								
	SC								
	PO								
Chromodac-ryorrhetic	IV								
	IP		0.29 103						
	IM								
	SC								
	PO								
	IV								
	IP								
	IM								
	SC								
	PO								
	IV								
	IP								
	IM								
	SC								
	PO								

PROTOVERATRINE

(Provell, Puroverine, Veralba)

mg/kg		Mouse	Rat	Guinea Pig	Rabbit	Cat	Dog	Monkey	
Lethal Dose Y–LD_{50} Z–MLD	IV	Y0.05 639			Y0.05 641				
	IP	Y0.4 640							
	IM								
	SC		Y0.6 639		Y0.11 639	Y0.5 641			
	PO		Y5.0 639						
Cardiovascular	IV					0.002 279	0.001 642		
	IP								
	IM								
	SC								
	PO								
Respiratory (Depression)	IV						0.007 643		
	IP								
	IM								
	SC								
	PO								
	IV								
	IP								
	IM								
	SC								
	PO								

IN VITRO

mg %	Cardiac	Vascular	Gut	Uterine	Visceral	Skeletal		

PSEUDOEPHEDRINE

(Sudafed, d-ψ-Ephedrine, d-Isoephedrine)

mg/kg		Mouse	Rat	Guinea Pig	Rabbit	Cat	Dog	Monkey	
Lethal Dose Y–LD_{50} Z–MLD	IV				85 [149]		125 [149]		
	IP								
	IM								
	SC		650 [149]		400 [149]				
	PO	115.5 [149]							
Cardiovascular	IV					1 [149]			
	IP								
	IM								
	SC								
	PO								
Diuretic	IV						0.6 [149]		
	IP								
	IM								
	SC								
	PO								
	IV								
	IP								
	IM								
	SC								
	PO								

IN VITRO

mg %	Cardiac	Vascular	Gut	Uterine	Visceral	Skeletal		
Contractile				0.3 [149]	0.2 [149]			

mg/kg		Mouse	Rat	Guinea Pig	Rabbit	Cat	Dog	Monkey	
Lethal Dose Y-LD_{50} Z-MLD	IV	Y74 [115]	Y75 [115]						
	IP								
	IM								
	SC								
	PO								
Cardiovascular	IV						100 [158]		
	IP								
	IM								
	SC								
	PO								
	IV								
	IP								
	IM								
	SC								
	PO								
	IV								
	IP								
	IM								
	SC								
	PO								

IN VITRO

mg %	Cardiac	Vascular	Gut	Uterine	Visceral	Skeletal		
Antiserotonergic			*0.0005 [644]	*0.00003 [644]				

*Total mg

PSILOCYBIN

mg/kg		Mouse	Rat	Guinea Pig	Rabbit	Cat	Dog	Monkey	
Lethal Dose Y—LD_{50} Z—MLD	IV	Y285 [115]	Y280 [115]						
	IP								
	IM								
	SC								
	PO								
Behavioral	IV								
	IP		100 [155]						
	IM								
	SC								
	PO								
Cardiovascular	IV						0.2 [158]		
	IP		0.15 [155]						
	IM								
	SC								
	PO								
Pentobarbital EEG Antagonist	IV				0.32 [159]				
	IP								
	IM								
	SC								
	PO								

IN VITRO

mg %	Cardiac	Vascular	Gut	Uterine	Visceral	Skeletal		
Antiserotonergic			*0.006 [644]	0.001 [644]				

*Total mg

mg/kg		Mouse	Rat	Guinea Pig	Rabbit	Cat	Dog	Monkey	
Respiratory (Depression)	IV						0.5 645		
	IP								
	IM								
	SC								
	PO								
Increased Flexor Reflex	IV					0.2			
	IP								
	IM								
	SC								
	PO								
	IV								
	IP								
	IM								
	SC								
	PO								
	IV								
	IP								
	IM								
	SC								
	PO								

IN VITRO

mg %	Cardiac	Vascular	Gut	Uterine	Visceral	Skeletal		

PYRILAMINE

(Anthisan, Mepyramine, Neo-Antergan)

mg/kg		Mouse	Rat	Guinea Pig	Rabbit	Cat	Dog	Monkey	
Lethal Dose Y–LD_{50} Z–MLD	IV	Y30 324		Y24.4 629					
	IP	Y102 646							
	IM								
	SC	Y150 324	Y150 647	Y70 324					
	PO	Y235 58							
Antihistaminic	IV						5 649		
	IP								
	IM						75 97		
	SC			1.3 58			75 97		
	PO			11.3 648			*125 97		
Sympatho- mimetic (Sensitization)	IV					5 144			
	IP								
	IM								
	SC								
	PO								
	IV								
	IP								
	IM								
	SC								
	PO								

*Total dose

IN VITRO

mg %	Cardiac	Vascular	Gut	Uterine	Visceral	Skeletal		
Antihistaminic			0.003					

PYROCATECHOL

(Catechol, Pyrocatechin)

mg/kg		Mouse	Rat	Guinea Pig	Rabbit	Cat	Dog	Monkey	
Lethal Dose Y–LD_{50} Z–MLD	IV						45 [651]		
	IP			150 [205]					
	IM								
	SC	150 [195]	225 [650]	225 [650]					
	PO		Y3890		1000 [346]				
Cardiovascular	IV						100 [652]		
	IP		12 [328]						
	IM								
	SC								
	PO								
CNS (Stimulation)	IV					5 [653]			
	IP								
	IM								
	SC								
	PO								
	IV								
	IP								
	IM								
	SC								
	PO								

IN VITRO

mg %	Cardiac	Vascular	Gut	Uterine	Visceral	Skeletal		
Langendorff	*30 [652]							
Depressant	** 6 [652]							

*Total mg
**mmol/L

PYROGALLOL

(Pyrogallic Acid)

mg/kg		Mouse	Rat	Guinea Pig	Rabbit	Cat	Dog	Monkey	
Lethal Dose Y—LD50 Z—MLD	IV						Z90 651		
	IP								
	IM								
	SC		Z650 650	Z1000 650			Z350 654		
	PO				Z1100 109		Z25 346		
Cardiovascular	IV		45			4 655	25 282		
	IP								
	IM								
	SC								
	PO								
Catechol-o-methyl Transferase Inhibition	IV					4 655			
	IP	*10 656	200 811						
	IM								
	SC								
	PO								
Chloral Hydrate Potentiation	IV								
	IP	50 342							
	IM								
	SC								
	PO								
	IV								
	IP								
	IM								
	SC								
	PO								
	IV								
	IP								
	IM								
	SC								
	PO								

*Total dose

QUINIDINE

(Quinicardine)

mg/kg		Mouse	Rat	Guinea Pig	Rabbit	Cat	Dog	Monkey	
Lethal Dose Y−LD_{50} Z−MLD	IV	Y69 555	Y23.1 363			Y21.6 658			
	IP	Y190 555	Z174 657						
	IM	Y200							
	SC	Z400 657							
	PO	Y593.9 555	Y1000 363						
Block Atrial Flutter	IV			5		2 659	3		
	IP								
	IM								
	SC								
	PO								
Cardiovascular	IV					10 659	15 363		
	IP								
	IM								
	SC								
	PO								
Nictitating Membrane Relaxation	IV					10 363	15 363		
	IP								
	IM								
	SC								
	PO								

IN VITRO

mg %	Cardiac	Vascular	Gut	Uterine	Visceral	Skeletal		
Guinea Pig				2				
Rabbit	5		1					

QUINIDINE (continued)

mg/kg		Mouse	Rat	Guinea Pig	Rabbit	Cat	Dog	Monkey	
Carotid Sinus Reflex Depressant	IV								
	IP								
	IM								
	SC								
	PO						30 [363]		
	IV								
	IP								
	IM								
	SC								
	PO								
	IV								
	IP								
	IM								
	SC								
	PO								
	IV								
	IP								
	IM								
	SC								
	PO								

IN VITRO

mg %	Cardiac	Vascular	Gut	Uterine	Visceral	Skeletal		

RESERPINE

(Sandril, Serpasil, Serpasol)

mg/kg		Mouse	Rat	Guinea Pig	Rabbit	Cat	Dog	Monkey	
Lethal Dose $Y-LD_{50}$ Z-MLD	IV		Y18 93				Y0.5 93		
	IP								
	IM								
	SC								
	PO	Y500 176							
Sedative	IV				3.5 661	1 634	0.05		
	IP	2.5 79					0.05	5 161	
	IM	2 477							
	SC	2.5 93	5 660						
	PO	10 474		4		10 634	0.65 93		
Serotonin and Norepinephrine Depletion	IV		0.4 662		5 667	3 91	5		
	IP		5 663	2.3 665		3 668	0.1 669		
	IM								
	SC		5 664	0.1 666		5	5		
	PO								
Behavioral	IV		0.2 670						
	IP	6 137	5 106						
	IM		1 260			5 487		0.75 671	
	SC	2 561	1.2 596						
	PO								
CNS	IV				2 509	1 396			
	IP					0.2 447			
	IM								
	SC								
	PO								
Barbituate Sleep Potentiation	IV		5 233						
	IP	5 469	5 411						
	IM								
	SC								
	PO								

mg/kg		Mouse	Rat	Guinea Pig	Rabbit	Cat	Dog	Monkey	
Catatonic	IV								
	IP		5 [165]						
	IM								
	SC								
	PO								
Cardiovascular	IV		1	1	1 [640]	1 [634]	1 [640]		
	IP		2.5		0.55 [457]				
	IM								
	SC								
	PO						1 [640]		
	IV								
	IP								
	IM								
	SC								
	PO								
	IV								
	IP								
	IM								
	SC								
	PO								

IN VITRO

mg %	Cardiac	Vascular	Gut	Uterine	Visceral	Skeletal		
Rabbit			0.1					
Antiserotonergic			3.0 [92]					

SCOPOLAMINE

(Hyosine, Scopos)

mg/kg		Mouse	Rat	Guinea Pig	Rabbit	Cat	Dog	Monkey	
Lethal Dose Y–LD_{50} Z–MLD	IV								
	IP								
	IM								
	SC	Y590 672							
	PO								
Anticholinergic	IV								
	IP								
	IM								
	SC	5 673				0.5			
	PO		1.5 144						
Sedative	IV						1		
	IP								
	IM								
	SC	450 672	13 674				1		
	PO								
Increased Muscle Activity	IV								
	IP								
	IM								
	SC	20 176	5 491						
	PO		10 491						
EEG (Synchronization)	IV				0.08 675	0.1 184			
	IP								
	IM								
	SC								
	PO								
Behavioral	IV								
	IP		1.8 106					0.1 185	
	IM								
	SC								
	PO								

mg/kg		Mouse	Rat	Guinea Pig	Rabbit	Cat	Dog	Monkey	
Anticonvulsant	IV								
	IP	5 251							
	IM								
	SC								
	PO								
	IV								
	IP								
	IM								
	SC								
	PO								
	IV								
	IP								
	IM								
	SC								
	PO								
	IV								
	IP								
	IM								
	SC								
	PO								

IN VITRO

mg %	Cardiac	Vascular	Gut	Uterine	Visceral	Skeletal		
Anticholinergic					$*2.5 \times 10^{-10}$			
Antihistaminic					$*7 \times 10^{-5}$			
Anti-$BaCl_2$					$*1 \times 10^{-4}$			

* M/L

SECOBARBITAL

(Evronal, Seconal, Seotal)

mg/kg		Mouse	Rat	Guinea Pig	Rabbit	Cat	Dog	Monkey	
Lethal Dose Y–LD_{50} Z–MLD	IV	Z80 [63]	Z35 [63]	Z35 [63]	Z45 [63]	Z50 [63]			
	IP	Z140 [63]	Z110 [63]	Z40 [63]	Z50 [63]	Z75 [63]			
	IM								
	SC	Z160 [63]	Z140 [63]	Z60 [63]	Z90 [63]				
	PO		Z125 [63]			Y50 [63]	Z90 [63]		
Anesthetic	IV	30 [63]	17.5 [63]	20 [63]	22.5 [72]	25 [63]		17.5 [63]	
	IP	60 [63]	40 [63]	20 [63]	30 [63]	35 [63]			
	IM								
	SC	70 [63]	60 [63]	30 [63]	50 [63]				
	PO		65 [63]	15 [76]			40 [63]		
Sedative	IV								
	IP		40 [63]						
	IM								
	SC		60 [63]						
	PO		65 [63]			3 [24]	3 [24]		
Serotonin Increase (Brain)	IV								
	IP		40						
	IM								
	SC								
	PO								
Flexor Reflex Inhibition	IV					5.4 [34]			
	IP								
	IM								
	SC								
	PO								
	IV								
	IP								
	IM								
	SC								
	PO								

SEMICARBAZIDE

(Aminourea, Carbamylhydrazine)

mg/kg		Mouse	Rat	Guinea Pig	Rabbit	Cat	Dog	Monkey	
Lethal Dose Y–LD_{50} Z–MLD	IV	Y125.6 550							
	IP	Y123.3 550							
	IM								
	SC	Y125.5 550							
	PO	Y176 550							
Convulsant	IV	111.7 550					10 550		
	IP	116.4 550	150 550	75 550	175 550	40 550		60 550	
	IM								
	SC								
	PO								
	IV								
	IP								
	IM								
	SC								
	PO								
	IV								
	IP								
	IM								
	SC								
	PO								

IN VITRO

mg %	Cardiac	Vascular	Gut	Uterine	Visceral	Skeletal		

SEROTONIN

(5-Hydroxytryptamine)

mg/kg		Mouse	Rat	Guinea Pig	Rabbit	Cat	Dog	Monkey	
Lethal Dose Y–LD50 Z–MLD	IV	Y160 814	Y30 814						
	IP	Y868 814	Y117 814						
	IM	Y750 119							
	SC								
	PO								
Cardiovascular Respiratory	IV		0.003		0.02 158	0.014 676	0.05 282		
	IP								
	IM								
	SC								
	PO								
Barbiturate Sleep Potentiation	IV		1.25 677						
	IP	8 98	10 286						
	IM								
	SC	50 286	50 286						
	PO								
EEG (Desynchronization)	IV				0.065 331	0.05 678			
	IP								
	IM								
	SC								
	PO								
Anticonvulsant	IV								
	IP								
	IM								
	SC		50 414						
	PO								
Decreased Cold Exposure Survival Time	IV								
	IP								
	IM								
	SC		2 679						
	PO								

mg/kg		Mouse	Rat	Guinea Pig	Rabbit	Cat	Dog	Monkey	
Decreased Caloric Intake	IV								
	IP								
	IM								
	SC		3 [680]						
	PO								
Antagonize Reserpine Ptosis	IV								
	IP	12.5 [78]							
	IM								
	SC								
	PO								
Increased Afferent Vagal Activity	IV					0.05 [292]	0.05 [631]		
	IP								
	IM								
	SC								
	PO								
	IV								
	IP								
	IM								
	SC								
	PO								

IN VITRO

mg %	Cardiac	Vascular	Gut	Uterine	Visceral	Skeletal		
Rat				0.012 [443]				
Guinea Pig			0.02					
Rabbit	*0.02 [67]							
Cat	*0.01 [292]							

*Total mg

SKF-525-A

(2-Diethylaminoethyl propyldiphenylacetate)

mg/kg		Mouse	Rat	Guinea Pig	Rabbit	Cat	Dog	Monkey	
Lethal Dose Y–LD_{50} Z–MLD	IV	Y60 115							
	IP	Y117.5 115	Y163 115						
	IM								
	SC								
	PO	Y538 115	Y2140 115						
Barbiturate Sleep Potentiation	IV								
	IP	10 681							
	IM								
	SC	50 118							
	PO								
	IV								
	IP								
	IM								
	SC								
	PO								
	IV								
	IP								
	IM								
	SC								
	PO								

IN VITRO

mg %	Cardiac	Vascular	Gut	Uterine	Visceral	Skeletal		

SODIUM BROMIDE

(Sedoneural)

mg/kg		Mouse	Rat	Guinea Pig	Rabbit	Cat	Dog	Monkey	
Lethal Dose Y–LD50 Z–MLD	IV		Z1800 53						
	IP								
	IM								
	SC								
	PO	Y7000 176	Y3500 682		Z580				
Sedative	IV						350		
	IP								
	IM								
	SC						350		
	PO	3000 176			5000	*150 24	*1500 24		
Anticonvulsant	IV				50				
	IP								
	IM								
	SC	60			150				
	PO	2000 550							
	IV								
	IP								
	IM								
	SC								
	PO								

*Total dose

IN VITRO

mg %	Cardiac	Vascular	Gut	Uterine	Visceral	Skeletal		

SODIUM FLUORIDE

(Florocid, Villiaumite)

mg/kg		Mouse	Rat	Guinea Pig	Rabbit	Cat	Dog	Monkey	
Lethal Dose $Y-LD_{50}$ Z−MLD	IV				87.5 [687]		Z80 [683]		
	IP	125 [109]	Z31 [683]						
	IM						Z40 [683]		
	SC	70 [346]	Z125 [684]	Z400 [686]		13.7 [109]	155 [109]		
	PO	80 [346]	Y200 [685]	Z250 [686]	Z200 [684]		Z75 [683]		
	IV								
	IP								
	IM								
	SC								
	PO								
	IV								
	IP								
	IM								
	SC								
	PO								
	IV								
	IP								
	IM								
	SC								
	PO								

IN VITRO

mg %	Cardiac	Vascular	Gut	Uterine	Visceral	Skeletal		

SODIUM NITRITE

(Erinitrit)

mg/kg		Mouse	Rat	Guinea Pig	Rabbit	Cat	Dog	Monkey	
Lethal Dose Y–LD_{50} Z–MLD	IV				Z85 [689]		Z15		
	IP								
	IM								
	SC		Z15 [688]		Z60 [109]	35 [690]	Z60 [691]		
	PO						Z330		
Cardiovascular	IV						10		
	IP		25 [7]						
	IM								
	SC		20 [539]				15		
	PO		40 [7]				*90		
Protect Against Cyanide	IV								
	IP								
	IM		10						
	SC								
	PO								
	IV								
	IP								
	IM								
	SC								
	PO								

*Total dose

IN VITRO

mg %	Cardiac	Vascular	Gut	Uterine	Visceral	Skeletal		
Rabbit		0.01	0.1					

SPARTEINE

(l-Sparteine, Lupinidine)

mg/kg		Mouse	Rat	Guinea Pig	Rabbit	Cat	Dog	Monkey	
Lethal Dose Y–LD_{50} Z–MLD	IV				Z30 109				
	IP								
	IM								
	SC	Z120 692			Z100 109				
	PO								
Cardiovascular	IV				5 693	5 694	5 694		
	IP								
	IM						10 693		
	SC						20 693		
	PO						60 693		
Ganglionic Block	IV					1 694			
	IP								
	IM								
	SC								
	PO								
	IV								
	IP								
	IM								
	SC								
	PO								

IN VITRO

mg %	Cardiac	Vascular	Gut	Uterine	Visceral	Skeletal		

STRYCHNINE

mg/kg		Mouse	Rat	Guinea Pig	Rabbit	Cat	Dog	Monkey	
Lethal Dose	IV	0.8 176	Z1.1 695		0.35 109	0.33 109	0.25 109		
Y–LD_{50}	IP	Y0.98 284	Y2.1 696						
Z–MLD	IM		Z4 697						
	SC	Y0.85 284	Y1.2 697	3.2 109	0.7 109	0.75 109	0.35 109		
	PO		Y16.2 685		15 109	0.75 109	1.1 109		
Convulsant	IV								
	IP	*1.5							
	IM		4						
	SC	1.33	8 88		0.4 611		0.07		
	PO								
Analeptic	IV				0.6				
	IP								
	IM								
	SC						*0.95 97		
	PO					*0.3 97	*0.95 97		
	IV								
	IP								
	IM								
	SC								
	PO								

*Total dose

IN VITRO

mg %	Cardiac	Vascular	Gut	Uterine	Visceral	Skeletal		
Rabbit		1.0	1.0					

SUCCINYLCHOLINE

(Anectine, Quelicin, Suxamethonium)

mg/kg		Mouse	Rat	Guinea Pig	Rabbit	Cat	Dog	Monkey	
Lethal Dose Y–LD_{50} Z–MLD	IV	Y0.75 [111]			Y1 [281]		0.3 [281]		
	IP	Y4 [111]							
	IM								
	SC								
	PO	Y125 [111]							
Neuromuscular Block	IV	0.45 [557]	0.45 [557]		0.25 [557]	0.08 [557]	0.1		
	IP					1			
	IM								
	SC								
	PO				0.1				
Ataxic and Respiratory (Depression)	IV				0.075				
	IP								
	IM								
	SC						0.05		
	PO								
	IV								
	IP								
	IM								
	SC								
	PO								

IN VITRO

mg %	Cardiac	Vascular	Gut	Uterine	Visceral	Skeletal		

SYROSINGOPINE

(Singoserp, SU-3118)

mg/kg		Mouse	Rat	Guinea Pig	Rabbit	Cat	Dog	Monkey	
Lethal Dose Y–LD_{50} Z–MLD	IV		Y50 640				>3 640	>2 640	
	IP								
	IM								
	SC								
	PO								
Catechol Amine Depletion (Brain and Heart)	IV				1 700		0.5 700		
	IP	5 698	7.5 699						
	IM								
	SC								
	PO								
Sedative	IV				4.5 700		5 640	2 640	
	IP		30 699						
	IM								
	SC	25 640							
	PO						> 30 640		
Cardiovascular	IV						1 640		
	IP		0.95 699						
	IM								
	SC								
	PO						3 640		
	IV								
	IP								
	IM								
	SC								
	PO								
	IV								
	IP								
	IM								
	SC								
	PO								

TETRABENAZINE

(Nitoman, RO-1-9569)

mg/kg		Mouse	Rat	Guinea Pig	Rabbit	Cat	Dog	Monkey	
Lethal Dose $Y-LD_{50}$ $Z-MLD$	IV	Y150 [115]							
	IP								
	IM								
	SC	Y400 [115]							
	PO								
Brain Amine Depletion	IV				50 [601]				
	IP								
	IM								
	SC								
	PO								
Barbiturate Sleep Potentiation	IV				50 [601]				
	IP	40 [28]							
	IM								
	SC								
	PO								
Behavioral	IV				40 [703]				
	IP		0.5 [370]						
	IM								
	SC		8 [702]						
	PO								
Sedative	IV								
	IP		2.3						
	IM								
	SC							2 [702]	
	PO								
	IV								
	IP								
	IM								
	SC								
	PO								

TETRACAINE

(Amethocaine, Curtacain, Pantocaine)

mg/kg		Mouse	Rat	Guinea Pig	Rabbit	Cat	Dog	Monkey	
Lethal Dose Y–LD_{50} Z–MLD	IV	Y70 7		Y15.6 629	8		Y4.3 704		
	IP								
	IM			30 7					
	SC								
	PO								
Convulsant	IV		1.5 705						
	IP								
	IM								
	SC								
	PO								
Anticonvulsant	IV					0.8			
	IP								
	IM								
	SC	4.4 441							
	PO								
	IV								
	IP								
	IM								
	SC								
	PO								

IN VITRO

mg %	Cardiac	Vascular	Gut	Uterine	Visceral	Skeletal		

TETRAETHYLAMMONIUM

(Etamon, TEA)

mg/kg		Mouse	Rat	Guinea Pig	Rabbit	Cat	Dog	Monkey	
Lethal Dose Y-LD_{50} Z-MLD	IV	Y29 214	Y63 706		Y72 706		Y55 706		
	IP	Y56 214	Y115 706						
	IM								
	SC	102 707							
	PO	Y655 214							
Ganglionic Block	IV					10	10		
	IP								
	IM								
	SC								
	PO								
Cardiovascular	IV					3 708	5 708		
	IP								
	IM								
	SC								
	PO								
EKG	IV					25 709	25 709		
	IP								
	IM								
	SC								
	PO								
Catechol Amine Sensitization	IV				2.5 395	2.5 395			
	IP								
	IM								
	SC								
	PO								
Nictitating Membrane Potentiation	IV					2 395			
	IP								
	IM								
	SC								
	PO								

TETRAETHYLAMMONIUM (continued)

mg/kg		Mouse	Rat	Guinea Pig	Rabbit	Cat	Dog	Monkey	
	IV								
	IP								
	IM								
	SC								
	PO								
	IV								
	IP								
	IM								
	SC								
	PO								
	IV								
	IP								
	IM								
	SC								
	PO								
	IV								
	IP								
	IM								
	SC								
	PO								

IN VITRO

mg %	Cardiac	Vascular	Gut	Uterine	Visceral	Skeletal		
Contractile			0.75 388					
Adrenolytic			0.001 395					

TETRAMETHYLAMMONIUM
(TMA)

mg/kg		Mouse	Rat	Guinea Pig	Rabbit	Cat	Dog	Monkey	
Lethal Dose Y–LD_{50} Z–MLD	IV				1.5 [341]				
	IP								
	IM								
	SC	20 [710]			7 [710]				
	PO								
Ganglionic Stimulant	IV					1	0.25		
	IP								
	IM								
	SC								
	PO								
Decrease Blood Pressure in Experimental Hypertension	IV								
	IP								
	IM								
	SC								
	PO		3 [387]						
	IV								
	IP								
	IM								
	SC								
	PO								

IN VITRO

mg %	Cardiac	Vascular	Gut	Uterine	Visceral	Skeletal		

THALIDOMIDE

(Contergan, Distaval, K-17)

mg/kg		Mouse	Rat	Guinea Pig	Rabbit	Cat	Dog	Monkey	
Lethal Dose Y–LD_{50} Z–MLD	IV								
	IP	>4000 484							
	IM								
	SC								
	PO	>5000 484							
CNS (Depression)	IV								
	IP	500 124	550 124				65 124		
	IM					100 557	300 557		
	SC								
	PO	100 484		650 484					
Anticonvulsant	IV								
	IP	525 124							
	IM								
	SC								
	PO								
Decreased Motor Activity	IV								
	IP	1000 711							
	IM								
	SC								
	PO	400 484		650 484					
Barbiturate Sleep Potentiation	IV								
	IP	1000 711							
	IM								
	SC								
	PO	1600 484							
Block Stress-Induced Ulcer	IV								
	IP								
	IM								
	SC								
	PO	100 712							

mg/kg		Mouse	Rat	Guinea Pig	Rabbit	Cat	Dog	Monkey	
Potentiate Chlorpromazine and Reserpine Catatonia	IV								
	IP								
	IM								
	SC								
	PO	200 484							
	IV								
	IP								
	IM								
	SC								
	PO								
	IV								
	IP								
	IM								
	SC								
	PO								
	IV								
	IP								
	IM								
	SC								
	PO								

IN VITRO

mg %	Cardiac	Vascular	Gut	Uterine	Visceral	Skeletal		
Anticholinergic			3 484					
Antihistiminic			3 484					

THEOPHYLLINE

(Acet-Theocin)

mg/kg		Mouse	Rat	Guinea Pig	Rabbit	Cat	Dog	Monkey	
Lethal Dose Y–LD50 Z–MLD	IV		Z240		115 109				
	IP								
	IM								
	SC	Z200 7	Z325	185 109					
	PO				350 109	100 109			
Cardiovascular and Diuretic	IV				15	10			
	IP								
	IM								
	SC								
	PO		30						
Increased Motor Activity	IV								
	IP								
	IM								
	SC		20 180						
	PO								
	IV								
	IP								
	IM								
	SC								
	PO								

IN VITRO

mg %	Cardiac	Vascular	Gut	Uterine	Visceral	Skeletal		
Antiserotonergic			8.0 92					

THIOPENTAL

(Intraval, Nesdonal, Pentothal)

mg/kg		Mouse	Rat	Guinea Pig	Rabbit	Cat	Dog	Monkey	
Lethal Dose Y−LD_{50} Z−MLD	IV	Y112 713	Y67.5 111	Y55 7	Y40 111		Y55 111		
	IP	Y200 111	Y120 111	Y57.5 714					
	IM								
	SC								
	PO	Y350 111			Y600 111		Y150 111		
Anesthesic	IV	25 111	20 111	20 111	20 111	28 24	25 716		
	IP		40 674	55 111		60 557			
	IM								
	SC								
	PO		70 715				100 111		
Behavioral	IV				5 562				
	IP								
	IM								
	SC				20 562				
	PO								
Depressed Spinal Neuron E. P. S. P.	IV					40 717			
	IP								
	IM								
	SC								
	PO								
Decreased EEG Arousal to R. A. S. Stimulation	IV					20 112			
	IP								
	IM								
	SC								
	PO								
	IV								
	IP								
	IM								
	SC								
	PO								

TM-10

(Xylocholine)

mg/kg		Mouse	Rat	Guinea Pig	Rabbit	Cat	Dog	Monkey	
Lethal Dose Y–LD_{50} Z–MLD	IV								
	IP								
	IM								
	SC								
	PO	Y95 [718]							
Sympatholytic	IV					10 [719]			
	IP								
	IM								
	SC								
	PO					17.5 [720]			
Tyramine Potentiation (B. P.)	IV					5			
	IP								
	IM								
	SC								
	PO								
Adrenal Medulla Catechol Amine Depletion	IV								
	IP								
	IM								
	SC		10 [721]						
	PO								

IN VITRO

mg %	Cardiac	Vascular	Gut	Uterine	Visceral	Skeletal		
Adrenolytic [812]			0.5					
Guinea Pig			5 [148]					

mg/kg		Mouse	Rat	Guinea Pig	Rabbit	Cat	Dog	Monkey	
Lethal Dose	IV	Y6.62 [722]							
Y–LD_{50}	IP								
Z–MLD	IM								
	SC								
	PO	1400 [722]							
Autonomic	IV	4.7 [722]				5 [722]	5 [722]		
	IP								
	IM								
	SC					3 [722]			
	PO					11.3 [720]			
Behavioral	IV								
	IP		30 [722]						
	IM								
	SC								
	PO								
	IV								
	IP								
	IM								
	SC								
	PO								

IN VITRO

mg %	Cardiac	Vascular	Gut	Uterine	Visceral	Skeletal		
Inhibition [812]			10 [722]					

TOLAZOLINE

(Artonil, Priscoline, Vasodil)

mg/kg		Mouse	Rat	Guinea Pig	Rabbit	Cat	Dog	Monkey	
Lethal Dose Y–LD_{50} Z–MLD	IV		67 640						
	IP	Y500							
	IM								
	SC								
	PO								
Adrenolytic	IV			1		1	2.5		
	IP		10 219						
	IM								
	SC								
	PO								
Cardiovascular (Reserpinized)	IV				2 383	1 640	1 640		
	IP								
	IM								
	SC								
	PO								
CNS	IV		15 350						
	IP								
	IM								
	SC								
	PO								

IN VITRO

mg %	Cardiac	Vascular	Gut	Uterine	Visceral	Skeletal		
Rabbit	0.5		1.0					
Rabbit Ear		2 339						

TRANYLCYPROMINE

(Parnate, SKF-385)

mg/kg		Mouse	Rat	Guinea Pig	Rabbit	Cat	Dog	Monkey	
Lethal Dose Y–LD_{50} Z–MLD	IV	Y37 115							
	IP								
	IM								
	SC								
	PO	Y38 115							
Increased Catechol Amines (Brain)	IV				5 371				
	IP	10 433							
	IM								
	SC								
	PO		5 433						
Reverse Reserpine Depression	IV								
	IP	2.5 455							
	IM								
	SC								
	PO	2.5 455							
EEG	IV				2 331				
	IP								
	IM								
	SC								
	PO								
Cardiovascular	IV		5 218						
	IP								
	IM								
	SC								
	PO								
CNS Stimulation (with 5-HTP)	IV						4 160		
	IP								
	IM								
	SC								
	PO								

TREMORINE

mg/kg		Mouse	Rat	Guinea Pig	Rabbit	Cat	Dog	Monkey	
Lethal Dose Y–LD_{50} Z–MLD	IV								
	IP								
	IM								
	SC								
	PO								
Tremor and Decreased Brain Amines	IV	20 [723]	5-20 [724]	5-20 [724]		5-20 [724]	5-20 [724]	5-20 [724]	
	IP	5-20 [724]	5-20 [724]	20 [724]		5-20 [724]	5 [723]	5-20 [724]	
	IM	5-20 [724]	5-20 [724]	5-20 [724]		5-20 [724]	5-20 [724]	5-20 [724]	
	SC	20 [76]	5-20 [724]	5-20 [724]		5-20 [724]	5-20 [724]	5-20 [724]	
	PO	20 [723]	5-20 [724]	5-20 [724]		5-20 [724]	5-20 [724]	5-20 [724]	
Increased Brain Histamine	IV								
	IP								
	IM								
	SC		100						
	PO								
Convulsant	IV								
	IP	5.8 [139]							
	IM								
	SC								
	PO								
Analgetic	IV								
	IP								
	IM	5							
	SC								
	PO								
EEG	IV								
	IP					3 [725]			
	IM								
	SC								
	PO								

TRIBROMETHANOL

(Avertin, Bromethol, Narcolan)

mg/kg		Mouse	Rat	Guinea Pig	Rabbit	Cat	Dog	Monkey	
Lethal Dose Y–LD50 Z–MLD	IV				135 66	300 557	300 557		
	IP	600 66	550 726		400 66				
	IM								
	SC	500 66	730 727						
	PO		1000 728		2000 109	150 66			
Anesthetic	IV	120 66		100 66	80 66	100 557	125 557		
	IP	250 200	550 547		225 66				
	IM		400 547						
	SC				500 66				
	PO				600 66	100 66			
	IV								
	IP								
	IM								
	SC								
	PO								
	IV								
	IP								
	IM								
	SC								
	PO								

IN VITRO

mg %	Cardiac	Vascular	Gut	Uterine	Visceral	Skeletal		

TRIFLUOPERAZINE

(Eskazine, Stelazine, Terfluzine)

mg/kg		Mouse	Rat	Guinea Pig	Rabbit	Cat	Dog	Monkey	
Lethal Dose Y–LD_{50} Z–MLD	IV	Y36 82					Y60 82		
	IP								
	IM								
	SC								
	PO	Y442 82	Y740 82						
Behavior	IV								
	IP		1 577						
	IM								
	SC		0.43 95						
	PO	1 729							
Catatonic	IV								
	IP		165 227						
	IM								
	SC								
	PO	25 730	2.6 730					20 730	
Decreased Spontaneous Motor Activity	IV								
	IP								
	IM								
	SC								
	PO	10 730	2.5 730					10 730	
Barbiturate Sleep Potentiation	IV								
	IP	1 227							
	IM								
	SC								
	PO								
	IV								
	IP								
	IM								
	SC								
	PO								

TRIMETHADIONE

(Tridione, Trimedone, Trimetin)

mg/kg		Mouse	Rat	Guinea Pig	Rabbit	Cat	Dog	Monkey	
Lethal Dose Y–LD_{50} Z–MLD	IV	Y2000 [731]			Y1500 [731]				
	IP	Y1800 [111]			Y1500 [731]				
	IM								
	SC		Y2200 [111]						
	PO	Y2200 [111]							
Anticonvulsant	IV		200 [111]						
	IP	150 [592]	300 [111]		500				
	IM								
	SC	225			500				
	PO	400				30 [97]	30 [97]		
Hypnotic	IV	1500			750 [111]				
	IP	1500							
	IM								
	SC		1500 [63]						
	PO	1500							
	IV								
	IP								
	IM								
	SC								
	PO								

IN VITRO

mg %	Cardiac	Vascular	Gut	Uterine	Visceral	Skeletal		

TRIPELENNAMINE

(Dehistin, Pyribenzamine, Tonaril)

mg/kg		Mouse	Rat	Guinea Pig	Rabbit	Cat	Dog	Monkey	
Lethal Dose Y–LD_{50} Z–MLD	IV	Y17 [732]	Y13 [732]		9		42.7		
	IP	Y70 [732]							
	IM								
	SC	Y75 [324]	Y225 [324]	Y30.2 [221]	33 [324]				
	PO	Y210 [324]	Y570 [324]	Y155 [221]					
Antihistaminic	IV			19 [221]		5.5 [97]	5.5 [97]		
	IP			10					
	IM			5					
	SC			5					
	PO			5.3 [648]		5.5 [97]	5.5 [97]		
Cardiovascular Potentiation of Aldehydes and Norepinephrine	IV					2 [496]	4 [263]		
	IP								
	IM								
	SC								
	PO								
	IV								
	IP								
	IM								
	SC								
	PO								

IN VITRO

mg %	Cardiac	Vascular	Gut	Uterine	Visceral	Skeletal		
Antiserotonergic			0.1 [92]					
Antihistaminic			0.005 [93]					
Anticholinergic			6 [93]					

TUBOCURARINE

(Delacurarine, Tubadil, Tubarine)

mg/kg		Mouse	Rat	Guinea Pig	Rabbit	Cat	Dog	Monkey	
Lethal Dose Y–LD_{50} Z–MLD	IV	0.14 733		0.1 736	Y0.35 735		3		
	IP	Y0.14 734	Y0.25 735						
	IM						10 111		
	SC	0.53 733	0.3	0.1 109	0.34 109	0.34 109	0.34 109		
	PO								
Neuromuscular Block	IV	0.075 736	0.075 736	0.035 736	0.12 735	0.15	0.1	0.75 442	
	IP								
	IM				0.4 736	0.7 557	0.15		
	SC				0.5 361		0.15		
	PO								
Cardiovascular	IV					0.1 736	0.1 736		
	IP								
	IM								
	SC								
	PO								
	IV								
	IP								
	IM								
	SC								
	PO								

IN VITRO

mg %	Cardiac	Vascular	Gut	Uterine	Visceral	Skeletal		
Phrenic Nerve-Diaphragm						0.16		
Rabbit	0.1		0.1					

TYRAMINE

(Systogene, Tocosine, Uteramine)

mg/kg		Mouse	Rat	Guinea Pig	Rabbit	Cat	Dog	Monkey	
Lethal Dose Y–LD50 Z–MLD	IV				300 [109]				
	IP								
	IM								
	SC	225 [109]				30 [109]			
	PO								
Cardiovascular	IV		0.1		0.1	0.5	0.25 [408]		
	IP								
	IM								
	SC	30 [737]							
	PO								
Decreased Tissue Uptake of Norepinephrine	IV					10 [91]			
	IP	80 [338]							
	IM		20 [738]						
	SC								
	PO								
	IV								
	IP								
	IM								
	SC								
	PO								

IN VITRO

mg %	Cardiac	Vascular	Gut	Uterine	Visceral	Skeletal		
Rat	0.002 [301]							
Ear–Rabbit		*0.016 [339]						
Langendorff	*0.01 [739]							

*Total mg

URETHAN(E)

(Ethyl Carbamate)

mg/kg		Mouse	Rat	Guinea Pig	Rabbit	Cat	Dog	Monkey	
Lethal Dose Y–LD_{50} Z–MLD	IV				2000				
	IP	Z2150 194							
	IM								
	SC		1800						
	PO						2500		
Anesthetic	IV				1000	1250	1000 413		
	IP		780 127	1500	1000	1500			
	IM		950 166			1800	1000		
	SC		950 166		1500	1000 740			
	PO					750	1500 550		
Sedative	IV								
	IP								
	IM								
	SC								
	PO					*1250 97	*1250 97		
	IV								
	IP								
	IM								
	SC								
	PO								

*Total dose

IN VITRO

mg %	Cardiac	Vascular	Gut	Uterine	Visceral	Skeletal		

VERATRIDINE

mg/kg		Mouse	Rat	Guinea Pig	Rabbit	Cat	Dog	Monkey	
Lethal Dose Y−LD_{50} Z−MLD	IV	Y0.42 [639]							
	IP	Y1.35 [640]	Y3.5 [639]						
	IM								
	SC								
	PO								
Cardiovascular	IV					*0.07 [741]	0.005 [742]		
	IP								
	IM								
	SC								
	PO								
Respiratory (Depression)	IV								
	IP						0.6 [643]		
	IM								
	SC								
	PO								
	IV								
	IP								
	IM								
	SC								
	PO								

*Total dose

IN VITRO

mg %	Cardiac	Vascular	Gut	Uterine	Visceral	Skeletal		

WARFARIN

(Coumadin, Maveran, Prothromadin)

mg/kg		Mouse	Rat	Guinea Pig	Rabbit	Cat	Dog	Monkey	
Lethal Dose Y–LD_{50} Z–MLD	IV	Y165 [111]	Y186 [743]		Y150 [743]		Y250 [743]		
	IP								
	IM								
	SC								
	PO	Y374 [743]	Y323 [743]	Y182 [743]	Y800 [743]		Y250 [743]		
	IV								
	IP								
	IM								
	SC								
	PO								
	IV								
	IP								
	IM								
	SC								
	PO								
	IV								
	IP								
	IM								
	SC								
	PO								

IN VITRO

mg %	Cardiac	Vascular	Gut	Uterine	Visceral	Skeletal		
Ionotropic (Negative)	25 [744]							

YOHIMBINE

(Aphrodine, Corynine, Quebrachine)

mg/kg		Mouse	Rat	Guinea Pig	Rabbit	Cat	Dog	Monkey	
Lethal Dose Y–LD_{50} Z–MLD	IV	16 [745]			11 [109]				
	IP								
	IM								
	SC				50 [109]		20 [346]		
	PO	40 [346]							
Adrenolytic	IV		5		2		0.2 [746]		
	IP								
	IM								
	SC								
	PO								
CNS	IV								
	IP	5 [350]							
	IM								
	SC		5 [350]						
	PO								
	IV								
	IP								
	IM								
	SC								
	PO								

IN VITRO

mg %	Cardiac	Vascular	Gut	Uterine	Visceral	Skeletal		
Antiserotonergic			0.5 [92]					

ZOXAZOLAMINE

(Flexin, McN-485, Contrazole)

mg/kg		Mouse	Rat	Guinea Pig	Rabbit	Cat	Dog	Monkey	
Lethal Dose Y–LD_{50} Z–MLD	IV								
	IP	Y376 461	Y102 461						
	IM								
	SC								
	PO	Y825 461	Y376 461						
Loss of Righting Reflex	IV								
	IP	81 461	43 461						
	IM								
	SC								
	PO	415 461	137 461						
Decrease Decerebrate Rigidity	IV					30 191			
	IP								
	IM								
	SC								
	PO	120 191							
Crossed-Extensor Reflex Depressant	IV					60			
	IP								
	IM								
	SC								
	PO								
Antistrychnine	IV								
	IP	227 461							
	IM								
	SC								
	PO								
	IV								
	IP								
	IM								
	SC								
	PO								

APPENDIX A

HORMONE MAINTENANCE AND REPLACEMENT DOSAGE

Species	Effect of Hormone	Dose	Route	Reference
	Hypophysectomized			
Mouse	Double Uterine Weight			
	Pregnant mare's serum gonadotrophin	1.8 IU	SC	754
Rat	Restore spermatogenesis			
	Testosterone propionate	3 mg/day/35 days	IP	755
	Stimulate ovarian growth			
	Diethylstilbestrol	1 mg/day/8 days	SC	756
	Estradiol	1 mg/day/8 days	SC	756
	Restore fatty acid synthesis			
	Thyroxine	0.1 mg/kg/day	IP	757
	ACTH	0.05 mg/day/14 days	IP	758
	Return O_2 consumption to normal			
	Thyroxine	0.01 mg/day	SC	759
	Corticosterone	1 mg/day/14 days	SC	760
	Cortisone Acetate	1 mg/day/14 days	SC	760
	Hydrocortisone Acetate	1 mg/day/14 days	SC	760
	Increase body weight to normal			
	Somatotropin	0.125 mg/halfday	SC	761
	(plus) Corticosterone	0.015 mg/halfday		
	(and) Thyroxine	0.003 mg/halfday		
Dog	Restore normal carbohydrate metabolism			
	Cortisone	1 mg/kg/day	IM	762
	Hydrocortisone	1 mg/kg/day	IM	762
	Produce hyperthyroid state			
	Thyroxin	0.4 mg/kg/day	IM	762
	Pancreatectomized			
Rat	Maintain weight			
	Insulin	1 unit/halfday	SC	763
	Maintain glucosurea			
	Insulin	18 units/day	SC	764
	Maintain serum gamma globulin during stress			
	Insulin	0.033 unit/halfday	SC	765

Species	Effect of Hormone	Dose	Route	Reference
	Pancreatectomized (continued)			
Rat (cont'd)	Exacerbation of urinary glucose			
	Progesterone	50 mg/day	SC	766
	11-Desoxycorticosterone acetate	10 mg/day	SC	767
Rabbit	Maintain weight on carbohydrate diet			
	Insulin	12 units/day	SC	768
Dog	Decrease glucose content of blood			
	Testosterone propionate	40 mg	IM	769
Baboon	Control diabetes			
	Insulin	2.5 units/kg/day	IV	770
	Adrenalectomized			
Rat	Maintenance dose			
	Hydrocortisone	0.1 mg/halfday	SC	771
	Cortexone acetate	0.1 mg/day	SC	772
	Diethylstilbestrol	0.1 mg/day	SC	773
	Return blood sugar to normal			
	Aldosterone	0.1 mg/day/9 days	SC	774
	Hydrocortisone acetate	15 mg/day/3 days	SC	775
	Return spontaneous activity to normal			
	Cortisone	5 mg/day/10 days	SC, PO	776
	Hydrocortisone	5 mg/day/10 days	SC	777
	Restore normal metabolism in adipose tissue			
	Dexamethasone	10 μg	IP	778
	Increase blood protein			
	Aldosterone	0.1 mg/day/12 days	SC	779
	Return plasma Na to normal			
	Aldosterone acetate	0.5 mg/kg	SC	780
	Block increase in antibody formation			
	Cortisone	80 mg/kg	SC	781
	Decrease heat loss on exposure to cold			
	Cortisone	1 mg/day	SC	782
	Adrenal cortical extract	0.25 mg/day	SC	782
	Prevent involution of pancreas acinar cells			
	Cortisone	0.5 mg/halfday	SC	783
Guinea Pig	Maintenance dose			
	Deoxycorticosterone	1 mg/day	SC	784
	Anesthetic dose			
	Deoxycortisone glucoside	100 mg	SC	784
Cat	Retard salivary gland atrophy			
	Deoxycorticosterone	5.0 mg/kg/day	SC	782
Dog	Maintenance dose			
	Cortisone acetate	25 mg/day	PO	785
	(plus) Desoxycosticosterone acetate-1	2 mg/day	IM	785
	Desoxycorticosterone acetate	2.5 mg/day	IM	762

Species	Effect of Hormone	Dose	Route	Reference
	Castrated			
Mouse	Maintenance dose			
	Testosterone phenylacetate	1.0 mg/10 days	SC	249
	Produce female-like mammary development			
	Estrone	92.5 μg	SC	786
Rat	Maintenance dose			
	Testosterone phenylacetate	50 mg/kg	SC	787
	Increase weight of seminal vesicles			
	Testosterone	0.4 mg/day/7 days	SC	788
	Testosterone	1.0 mg/day/7 days	IP, PO	788
	Testosterone propionate	0.5 mg/day/20 days	SC	789
	Testosterone propionate	0.4 mg/day/7 days	IP	788
	Testosterone propionate	1.0 mg/day/7 days	PO	788
	Methyltestosterone	0.4 mg/day/7 days	SC, IP, PO	788
	Inhibit calcium loss			
	Testosterone	2 mg/day	SC	790
	Return of spontaneous activity to normal			
	Testosterone propionate	20 mg/day/10 days	SC	776
	Prevent prostatic epithelial cell atrophy			
	Testosterone	100 μg/kg/day	SC	791
Guinea Pig	Return seminal vesicle weight and metabolism to normal			
	Testosterone propionate	2 mg/day	SC	792
	Diminish the fall in hepatic glycogen			
	Testosterone	15 mg/2 days/30 days	SC	793
	Decrease nondirected hyperexcitability			
	Testosterone	250 μg/kg/day	SC	794
	Ovariectomized			
Mice	Induce mammary growth in immature			
	Estrone	0.006 μg/day/21 days	SC	795
Rat	Hormone replacement			
	Estradiol benzoate	0.015 mg/kg/day	SC	796
	Polyestradiol phosphate	20 mg/kg/day	SC	787
	Increase vaginal cornification and activity			
	Dienestral	1 μg/day/10 days	PO, SC	776
	Hexestral	1 μg/day/10 days	SC	776
	Hexestral	40 μg/day/10 days	PO	776
	Stilbestrol	1 μg/day/10 days	SC	776
	Stilbestrol	4 μg/day/10 days	PO	776
	Pregnancy maintenance			
	Acetonide	10 mg/day	SC, PO	797
	Acetophenone	20 mg/day	SC, PO	797
	Progesterone	20 mg/day	SC, PO	797
	Return spontaneous activity to normal			
	Estrone benzoate	1 mg/day/10 days	SC	776
	Lower ECS threshold			
	Estradiol	5 mg/kg/day/7 days	SC	798

HORMONE MAINTENANCE AND REPLACEMENT DOSAGE

Species	Effect of Hormone	Dose	Route	Reference
	Thyroidectomized			
Rat	Maintenance dose			
	Thyroxine	0.005 mg/day	IP	799
	Return metabolic rate to normal			
	Thyroxine	0.015 mg/kg/day	IP	800
	Improve or normalize glucose tolerance			
	Triiodothyroxine	0.02 mg/day/4 days	SC	801
Guinea Pig	Increase metabolism			
	Thyrotropic hormone	25 units/day/12 days	IM	802
	Thyroparathyroidectomized			
Rat	Replacement therapy in lactating female			
	Thyroxin	30 μg/kg/day	SC	
	(plus) Parathyroid hormone	300 USPU/kg/day	SC	803
	Produce arthritis			
	Deoxycorticosterone acetate	2 mg/day	SC	804
Dog	Return intestinal Ca absorption to normal			
	Parathyroid extract	500 IU	IV	805
	Parathyroidectomized			
Rat	Increase excretion of urinary phosphate			
	Parathyroid hormone	20 USPU	SC	806
	Parathyroid hormone	1.0 IU/hour	SC	807
	Cortisone	10 mg/day	IP	808

APPENDIX B

PHYSIOLOGICAL SOLUTIONS
(Gm/liter)

	Saline (Mammal)	Ringer (Mammal)	Feigen's (Isolated Heart)	Locke Ringer (Isolated Uterus)	Tyrodes (Isolated Gut)
NaCl	9.00	9.00	9.00	9.00	8.00
KCl	----	0.42	0.42	0.42	0.20
$CaCl_2$	----	0.24	0.62	0.24	0.20
$MgCl_2$	----	----	----	----	0.10
$NaHCO_3$	----	0.30	0.60	0.50	1.00
NaH_2PO_4	----	----	----	----	0.05
Glucose	----	----	1.00	1.00	2.00

BIBLIOGRAPHY

1. Skog, E. A Toxicological Investigation of Lower Aliphatic Aldehydes. I. Toxicity of Formaldehyde, Acetaldehyde, Propionaldehyde and Butyraldehyde; as well as of Acrolein and Crotonaldehyde. Acta pharmacol. (Kbh.) 6: 299-318, 1950.

2. Stotz, E., et al. Behavioral and Pharmacological Studies of Thiopropazate, a Potent Tranquilizing Agent. Arch. int. Pharmacodyn. 127:85-103, 1960.

3. Supniewski, J. V. The Toxic Action of Acetaldehyde on the Organs of Vertebrata. J. Pharmacol. exp. Ther. 30:429-437, 1927.

4. Sollmann, T. H. and P. J. Hanzlik. Fundamentals of Experimental Pharmacology. J. W. Stacey, Inc., San Francisco, 1940.

5. Eade, N. R. Mechanism of Sympathomimetic Action of Aldehydes. J. Pharmacol. exp. Ther. 127:29-34, 1959.

6. Kreitmair, D. H. The Pharmacological Action of Ephedrine. Arch. exp. Path. Pharmakol. 120:189-228, 1927.

7. Anderson, H. H., et al. Pharmacology and Experimental Therapeutics. University of California Press, Berkeley and Los Angeles, 1947.

8. Smith, P. K. and W. E. Hambourger. The Ratio of the Toxicity of Acetanilid to its Antipyretic Activity in Rats. J. Pharmacol. exp. Ther. 54:159-160, 1935.

9. Smith, P. K. and W. E. Hambourger. The Ratio of the Toxicity of Acetanilide and its Antipyretic Activity in Rats. J. Pharmacol. exp. Ther. 54:346-351, 1935.

10. Lester, D. Formation of Methemoglobin. J. Pharmacol. exp. Ther. 77:154-159, 1943.

11. Munch, J. C., et al. Acetanilid Studies. I. Acute Toxicity. J. Amer. pharm. Ass. 30:91-98, 1941.

12. Karczmar, A. G. The Effects of Lethal Doses of Acetanilid in the Dog. Fed. Proc. 6:341-343, 1947.

13. Molitor, H. A Comparative Study of the Effects of Five Choline Compounds Used in Therapeutics: Acetylcholine Chloride, Acetyl Beta-Methylcholine Chloride, Carbaminoyl Choline, Ethyl Ether Beta-Methyl-choline Chloride, Carbaminoyl Beta-Methylcholine Chloride. J. Pharmacol. exp. Ther. 58: 337-360, 1936.

14. Monnier, M. Electro-Physiological Actions of Central Nervous System Stimulants. Arch. int. Pharmacodyn. 124:281-301, 1960.

15. Trendelenburg, U. and J. S. Gravenstein. Effect of Reserpine Pretreatment on Stimulation of the Accelerans Nerve of the Dog. Science 128:901-902, 1958.

16. Fraser, P. J. Pharmacologic Actions of Pure Muscarine Chloride. Brit. J. Pharmacol. 12:47-52, 1957.

17. Ben-Bassat, J., et al. Analgesimetry and Ranking of Analgesic Drugs by the Receptacle Method. Arch. int. Pharmacodyn. 122:434-447, 1959.

18. Hart, E. R. The Toxicity and Analgetic Potency of Salicylamide and Certain of its Derivatives as Compared with Established Analgetic-Antipyretic Drugs. J. Pharmacol. exp. Ther. 89:205-209, 1947.

19. Ichniowski, C. T. and W. C. Hueper, Pharmacological and Toxicological Studies on Salicylamide. J. Am. pharm. Ass. 35: 225-230, 1946.

20. Eagle, E. and A. J. Carlson. Toxicity, Antipyretic and Analgesic Studies on 39 Compounds Including Aspirin, Phenacetin and 27 Derivatives of Carbazole and Tetrahydrocarbazole. J. Pharmacol. exp. Ther. 99:450-457, 1950.

21. Smith, C. S., et al. The Analgesic Properties of Certain Drugs and Drug Combinations. J. Pharmacol. exp. Ther. 77:184-193, 1943.

22. Winder, C. V. Quantitative Evaluation of Analgesic Action in Guinea Pigs. Morphine, Ethyl 1-Methyl-4-Phenylpiperidine-4-Carboxylate (Demerol) and Acetylsalicylic Acid. Arch. int. Pharmacodyn. 74:219-226, 1947.

23. Eillinger, A. Aromatic Hydrocarbons, Phenols, Aromatic Acids, Aromatic Alcohols, Aldehydes, Ketones, Quinines and Nitro Compounds. Heffter's Hdb. 1:871-1048, 1923.

24. Jones, L. M. Veterinary Pharmacology and Therapeutics. The Iowa State College Press, Ames, Iowa, 1957.

25. Guerra, F. and G. H. Barbour. The Mechanism of Aspirin Antipyresis in Monkeys. J. Pharmacol. exp. Ther. 79:55-61, 1943.

26. Collier, H. O. J., et al. The Bronchoconstrictor Action of Bradykinin in the Guinea Pig. Brit. J. Pharmacol. 15:290-297, 1960.

27. Launey, L. Determination of Toxicity and Activity of Several Barbiturate Derivatives. Principles of Comparison. J. Physiol. Path. gén. 30:364-378, 1932.

28. Pletscher, A., et al. Bensoquinolizine, a New Compound with an Action on 5-Hydroxytryptamine and Norepinephrine in the Brain. Arch. exp. Path. Pharmakol. 232:499-509, 1958.

29. Barlow, O. W. Studies on the Pharmacology of Ethyl Alcohol. I. A Comparative Study of the Pharmacologic Effects of Grain and Synthetic Ethyl Alcohols. II. A Correlation of the Local Irritant, Anesthetic and Toxic Effects of Three Potable Whiskeys with their Alcoholic Content. J. Pharmacol. exp. Ther. 56:117-146, 1936.

30. Alekseeva, I. A. The Direct and Conditioned Reflex Effects of Inhibitory Substances on the Higher Nervous Activity of Dogs with Organic Lesions of Certain Parts of the Cerebral Cortex. Pavlov J. higher nerv. Activ. 10:737-744, 1960.

31. Bonnycastle, D. D., et al. The Effect of a Number of Central Depressant Drugs upon Brain 5-Hydroxytryptamine Levels in the Rat. J. Pharmacol. exp. Ther. 135:17-20, 1962.

32. Miller, N. E. and H. Barry. Motivational Effects of Drugs: Some General Problems in Psychopharmacology. Psychopharmacologia 1:169-199, 1960.

33. Lehman, A. J. Chemicals in Food: A Report to the Association of Food and Drug Officials on Current Developments. Assoc. Food & Drug Officials U. S. Quart. Bull. 15:122-133, 1951.

34. Witkin, L. B., et al. A Study of Some Central Stimulants in Mice. Arch. int. Pharmacodyn. 124:105-115, 1960.

35. Hanzlik, P. J., et al. Toxicity, Fats and Excretion of Propylene Glycol and Some Other Glycols. J. Pharmacol. exp. Ther. 67:101-126, 1939.

36. Waisbren, B. A. Alloxan Diabetes in Mice. Proc. Soc. exp. Biol. (N. Y.) 67:154-156, 1948.

37. Gabe, M. Histological Changes of the Liver and Heart Following Acute Alloxan Intoxication in the Albino Rat. C. R. Soc. Biol. (Paris) 142:1335-1340, 1948.

38. Lazarow, A. Protective Effect of Glutathione against Alloxan Diabetes in the Rat. Proc. Soc. exp. Biol. (N. Y.) 61:441-447, 1946.

39. Gomeri, G. and M. G. Goldner. Production of Diabetes Mellitus in Rats with Alloxan. Proc. Soc. exp. Biol. (N. Y.) 54:287-290, 1943.

40. Duff, G. L. and H. Starr. Experimental Alloxan Diabetes in Hooded Rats. Proc. Soc. exp. Biol. (N. Y.) 57:280-282, 1944.

41. Goldner, M. G. and G. Gomori. Alloxan Diabetes in the Dog. Endocrinology 33:297-308, 1943.

42. Gruber, C. M., et al. Studies on the Pharmacology and Toxicology of dl-α-1, 3-Dimethyl-4-Phenyl-4-Propionoxy Piperidine (Nu-1196). J. Pharmacol. exp. Ther. 99:312-316, 1950.

43. Randall, L. O. and G. Lehman. Pharmacological Properties of Some Neostigmine Analogs. J. Pharmacol. exp. Ther. 99:16-32, 1950.

44. Maney, P. V., et al. Dihydroxypropyltheophylline: Its Preparation and Pharmacological

Clinical Study. J. Amer. pharm. Ass., sci. Ed. 35:266-272, 1946.

45. Thompson, C. R. and M. R. Warren. Acute and Chronic Toxicity Studies on Theophylline Aminoisobutanol and Theophylline Ethylenediamine. J. Lab. clin. Med. 31:1337-1343, 1946.

46. Warecka, K. The Influence of Euphylline, Chlorpromazine and Reserpine on the Pia Mater Blood Vessels of Cats and Rabbits. Acta physiol. pharmacol. neerl. 9:452-460, 1960.

47. Christensen, J. M., et al. Ethylnorephrine: A Unique Bronchodilator. Amer. Practit. 9: 916-921, 1958.

48. Cameron, W. M., et al. Further Evidences on the Nature of the Vasomotor Actions of Ethylnorsuprarenin. J. Pharmacol. exp. Ther. 63:340-351, 1938.

49. Koch, R. On the Toxicity of Pyramidon. Med. Klin. 45:661-665, 1950.

50. Domenjoz, R. The Pharmacology of Phenylbutazone Analogues. Ann. N.Y. Acad. Sci. 86: 263, 1960.

51. Rose, C. L. Detoxification of Amidopyrine by Sodium Amytal. Proc. Soc. exp. Biol. (N.Y.) 32:1242-1243, 1935.

52. Hazelton, L. W., et al. Acute and Chronic Toxicity of Butazolidin. J. Pharmacol. exp. Ther. 109:387-392, 1953.

53. Loeser, D. and A. L. Konwiser. A Study of the Toxicity of Strontium and Comparison with Other Cations Employed in Therapeutics. J. Lab. clin. Med. 15:35-41, 1929.

54. Horwitt, M. K., et al. Heat Regulation and Water Exchange. J. Pharmacol. exp. Ther. 48:217-222, 1933.

55. Winder, C. V., et al. A Study of Pharmacological Influences on Ultraviolet Erythema in Guinea Pigs. Arch. int. Pharmacodyn. 116: 261, 1958.

56. Filehne, W. Pyramidon. Z. klin. Med. 32: 569-577, 1897.

57. Biberfeld, J. Pharmacological Studies on Some Pyrazolon Derivatives. Zschr. exp. Path. 5:28-42, 1908.

58. Merck Institute. Personal Communication

59. Herr, F. et al. Tranquilizers and Antidepressants: A Pharmacological Comparison. Arch. int. Pharmacodyn. 134:328-342, 1961.

60. Steiner, W. G. and H. E. Himwich. Central Cholinolytic Action of Chlorpromazine. Science 136:873-875, 1962.

61. Feldman, S. A. Effect of Decamethonium upon Conditioned Reflexes in Rats. Anaesthesia 15:55-60, 1960.

62. Amberg, S. and H. F. Helmholz. The Fatal Dose of Various Substances on Intravenous Injection in the Guinea Pig. J. Pharmacol. exp. Ther. 6:595, 1915.

63. Swanson, E. E. and W. E. Fry. A Comparative Study of Two Short Acting Barbituric Acid Derivatives. J. Amer. pharm. Ass. 26:1248-1249, 1937.

64. Holck, H. G. and M. A. Kanan. Intravenous Lethal Doses of Amytal in the Dog and Rabbit and a Table of Animal Dosages Compiled from the Literature. J. Lab. clin. Med. 19: 1191-1205, 1934.

65. Butler, T. C. The Delay in Onset of Intravenously Injected Anesthetics. J. Pharmacol. exp. Ther. 74:118-128, 1942.

66. Heubner, W. and J. Schuller. Narcotics of the Aliphatic Series. Heffter's Hdb. E. 2:1-282, 1936.

67. Hirschfelder, A. D. and R. N. Bieter. Local Anesthetics. Physiol. Rev. 12:190-282, 1932.

68. Vogt, M. Comparative Studies in Circulatory Damage and Narcotic Effect of Various Barbituric Acid Derivatives. Arch exp. Path. Pharmakol. 152:341-360, 1930.

69. Swett, L. R., et al. Structure-Activity Relations in the Pargyline Series. Ann. N.Y. Acad. Sci. 107:891-898, 1963.

70. Gruber, C. M., et al. III. The Toxic Actions of Sodium Diphenyl Hydantoinate (Dilantin) when Injected Intraperitoneally and Intravenously in Experimental Animals. J. Pharmacol. exp. Ther. 68:433-436, 1940.

71. Maloney, A. H. Picrotoxin as an Antidote in Acute Poisoning by the Barbiturates. J. Pharmacol. exp. Ther. 42:267-268, 1931.

72. Gruber, C. M. and G. F. Keyser. A Study on the Development of Tolerance and Cross

Tolerance to Barbiturates in Experimental Animals. J. Phramacol. exp. Ther. 86:186-196, 1946.

73. Halpern, B. N. Toxicity and Cardiovascular Action of β-Phenylisopropylamine (Benzedrine). J. Physiol. Path. gén. 37:597-614, 1939.

74. Heubner, W. and M. Stuhlman. A Notice on Benzedrine and Pervitin. Arch. exp. Path. Pharmakol. 202:594-596, 1943.

75. Günther, B. Toxicity of Benzedrine Sulfate in the White Mouse and in the Frog (Calyptocephalus Gayi). J. Pharmacol. exp. Ther. 76: 375-377, 1942.

76. Frommel, E., et al. Pharmacological Study of Dextrorotatory and Levorotatory Pheneturide. Arch. int. Pharmacodyn. 122:15-31, 1959.

77. Chen, A. L. Preliminary Observations with Theophylline Mono-Ethanolamine. J. Pharmacol. exp. Ther. 45:1-5, 1932.

78. Garattini, S., et al. Antagonists of Reserpine Induced Eyelid Ptosis. Med. exp. (Basel) 3: 252-259, 1960.

79. Wilson, S. P. and R. Tislow. Differential Antagonism of Reserpine Eyelid Closure by Imipramine and Amphetamine. Proc. Soc. exp. Biol. (N. Y.) 109:847-848, 1962.

80. Swinyard, E. A., et al. Studies on the Mechanism of Amphetamine Toxicity in Aggregated Mice. J. Pharmacol. exp. Ther. 132:97-102, 1961.

81. Ehrich, W. E. and K. B. Krumbhaar. The Effects of Large Doses of Benzedrine Sulphate on the Albino Rat: Functional and Tissue Changes. Ann. intern. Med. 10:1874-1888, 1957.

82. Smith, Kline and French Laboratories. Personal Communication.

83. Ehrich, W. E. et al. Experimental Studies upon the Toxicity of Benzedrine Sulphate in Various Animals. Amer. J. med. Sci. 198: 785-803, 1939.

84. Searle, L. V. and C. W. Brown. Effect of Subcutaneous Injections of Benzedrine Sulfate on the Activity of White Rats. J. Exptl. Psychol. 22:480-490, 1938.

85. Garberg, L. and F. Sandberg. A Method for Quantitative Estimation of the Stimulant Effect of Analeptics on the Spontaneous Motility of Rats. Acta pharmacol. (Kbh.) 16:367-373, 1960.

86. Esser, A. Clinical, Anatomical and Spectrographic Investigations of the Central Nervous System in Acute Metal Poisoning with Particular Consideration of their Importance for Forensic Medicine and Industrial Pathology. Dtsch. Z. ges. gerichtl. Med. 25:239-317, 1935.

87. Munoz, C. and L. Goldstein. Influence of Adrenergic Blocking Drugs upon the EEG Analeptic Effect of dl-Amphetamine in Conscious Unrestrained Rabbits. J. Pharmacol. exp. Ther. 132:354-359, 1961.

88. Courvoisier, S. Pharmacodynamic Properties of the Chlorhydrate of Chloro-3 (Dimethyl-Amino-3' Propyl)-10 Phenothiazine (4.560 R.P.). Arch. int. Pharmacodyn. 92:305-361, 1953.

89. Cole, J. and P. Glees. Some Effects of Methyl-Phenidate (Ritalin) and Amphetamine on Normal and Neucotomized Monkeys. J. ment. Sci. 103:406-417, 1957.

90. Uyeda, A. and J. M. Fuster. The Effects of Amphetamine on Tachistoscopic Performance in the Monkey. Psychopharmacologia 3: 463-467, 1962.

91. Hertting, G. et al. Effect of Drugs on the Uptake and Metabolism of H^3-Norepinephrine. J. Pharmacol. exp. Ther. 134:146-153, 1961.

92. Jaques, R. 5-Hydroxytryptamine Antagonists, with Special Reference to the Importance of Sympathomimetic Amines and Isopropyl-Noradrenaline. Helv. physiol. pharmacol. Acta. 14:269-278, 1956.

93. Ciba Pharmaceutical Company. Personal Communication.

94. Orahovats, P. D., et al. Pharmacology of Ethyl-1-(4-Aminophenethyl)-4-Phenylisonipecotate, Anileridine, a New Potent Synthetic Analgesic. J. Pharmacol. exp. Ther. 119: 26-34, 1957.

95. Janssen, P. A. J., et al. Apomorphine-Antagonism in Rats. Arzneimittel-Forsch. 10:1003-1005, 1960.

96. Klee, P. and L. Laux. Further Investigations on Vomiting and the Action of Emetics. Deut. Arch. klin. Med. 149:189-208, 1925.

97. Seiden, R. Veterinary Drugs in Current Use. Springer, New York, 1960.

98. Dandiya, P. C. and E. A. Sellers. Mechanism of the Hypnosis Prolongation Action of 5-Hydroxytryptamine and Some Sympathomimetic Amines. Arch. int. Pharmacodyn. 130:32-41, 1961.

99. Cook, L. et al. Epinephrine, Norepinephrine and Acetylcholine as Conditioned Stimuli for Avoidance Behavior. Science 131:990-991, 1960.

100. Chang, V. and M. J. Rand. Transmission Failure in Sympathetic Nerves Produced by Hemicholinium. Brit. J. Pharmacol. 15:588-600, 1960.

101. Cahen, R. L. and K. Tvede. Homatropine Methyl-Bromide: A Pharmacological Reëvaluation. J. Pharmacol. exp. Ther. 105:166-177, 1952.

102. Randall, L. O. and G. Lehmann. Pharmacological Studies on Analgesic Piperidine Derivatives. J. Pharmacol. exp. Ther. 93:314-328, 1948.

103. Schwartz, A. A Comparison of Two in vivo Methods Used for Assaying Anti-Ulcer Potency. Arch. int. Pharmacodyn. 127:203-210, 1960.

104. Willberg, M. A. Natural Resistance of Several Animals toward Atropine. Biochem. Z. 66:389-407, 1914.

105. Frommel, E. and C. Fleury. On the Paradoxical Mechanism of the Potentiation of the Soporific Effect of Barbiturates by Belladonna. Med. exp. (Basel) 3:257-263, 1960.

106. Domer, F. R. and F. M. Schueler. Investigations of the Amnesic Properties of Scopolamine and Related Compounds. Arch. int. Pharmacodyn. 127:449-458, 1960.

107. Ficklewirth, G. and A. Heffter. Resistance of the Rabbit to Atropine. Biochem. Z. 40: 36-47, 1912.

108. White, R. P. and L. D. Boyajy. Neuropharmacological Comparison of Atropine, Scopolamine, Benactyzine, Diphenhydramine and Hydroxyzine. Arch. int. Pharmacodyn. 127:260-273, 1960.

109. Flury, F. and F. Zernik. Classification of Toxic and Lethal Doses for the Commonly Used Poisons and Research Animals. Abderhalden, Handbuch der biologischen Arbeitsmethoden. Abt. IV, Teil 7B:1289-1422, 1928.

110. Rice, W. B. and J. D. McColl. Antagonism of Psychotomimetic Agents in the Conscious Cat. Arch. int. Pharmacodyn. 127:249-259, 1960.

111. Abbott Laboratories. Personal Communication.

112. Loeb, C., et al. Electrophysiological Analysis of the Action of Atropine on the Central Nervous System. Rev. arch. ital. biol. 98:293-307, 1960.

113. Bainbridge, J. G. and D. M. Brown. Ganglion-Blocking Properties of Atropine-Like Drugs. Brit. J. Pharmacol. 15:147-151, 1960.

114. Paul-David, J., et al. Quantification of Effects of Depressant Drugs on EEG Activation Response. J. Pharmacol. exp. Ther. 129: 69-74, 1960.

115. Usdin, E. and R. L. S. Amasi. Psychotropic and Related Compounds. Psychopharmacology Service Center Bulletin 2:17-93, 1963.

116. Brown, B. B. The Pharmacologic Activity of α-(4-Piperidyl)-Benzhydrol Hydrochloride (Azacyclonol Hydrochloride): An Ataractic Agent. J. Pharmacol. exp. Ther. 118: 153-161, 1956.

117. Root, W. S. and F. G. Hofman. Physiological Pharmacology. Vol. 1: The Nervous System. Part A. Central Nervous System Drugs. Academic Press, New York and London, 1963.

118. Rümke, C. L. and J. Bout. The Influence of Previously Introduced Drugs on Hexobarbital Narcosis. Arch. exp. Path. Pharmakol. 240:218-223, 1960.

119. Tripod, J., et al. Experimental Differentiation of a Series of Central Nervous System Inhibitors. Arch. int. Pharmacodyn. 112:319-341, 1957.

120. Dhawan, B. N. and G. P. Gupta. Hypothermic and Antipyretic Activity of 4-Piperidyl Diphenyl Carbinol Hydrochloride (Azacyclonol). Arch. int. Pharmacodyn. 137:54-60, 1962.

121. Hahn, F. and A. Oberdorf. Comparative Investigations on the Antagonism of Bemegrid, Pentetrazol and Picrotoxin. Arch. int. Pharmacodyn. 135:9-30, 1962.

122. Gruber, C. M., et al. A Toxicological and Pharmacological Investigation of Sodium Sec-Butyl Ethyl Barbituric Acid (Butisol Sodium). J. Pharmacol. exp. Ther. 81:254-268, 1944.

123. MacFarlane, A. W. and J. S. McKenzie. The Pharmacology of a New Central Nervous System Stimulant, ββ Methyl Isopropyl Glutarimide. Arch. int. Pharmacodyn. 127:379-401, 1960.

124. Kuhn, W. L. and E. F. Von Maanen. Central Nervous System Effects of Thalidomide. J. Pharmacol. exp. Ther. 134:60-68, 1961.

125. Eddy, N. B. Studies of Morphine, Codeine and their Derivatives. IX. Methyl Ethers of the Morphine and Codeine Series. J. Pharmacol. exp. Ther. 55:127-135, 1935.

126. Underhill, F. P. and O. R. Johnson. A Comparative Study of New Ether Derivatives of Barbituric Acid. J. Pharmacol. exp. Ther. 35:441-448, 1929.

127. Lendle, L. Investigation on the Different Points of Attack of Some Narcotics in the Central Nervous System. Arch. exp. Path. Pharmakol. 143:108-116, 1929.

128. Jones, I. and E. V. Lynn. The Toxicity of Barbital Derivatives. J. Amer. pharm. Ass. 25:597-601, 1936.

129. Fitch, R. H. and E. E. McCandless. A Comparison of the Intraperitoneal and Oral Effects of the Barbituric Acid Derivatives. J. Pharmacol. exp. Ther. 42:266-267, 1931.

130. Elliott, K. A. C. and N. M. von Golder. The State of Factor I in Rat Brain: The Effects of Metabolic Conditions and Drugs. J. Physiol. (Lond.) 153:423-432, 1960

131. Schuster, R., et al. Pharmacological Data on the Analeptic Bemegride. Latvijas PSR Zinatnu Akad. 8:105-110, 1961.

132. Denisenko, P. P. The effect of Certain Esters of R, R'-Aminoethanol and Diphenylacetic Acid on the Central Nervous System. Farmakol. i Toksikol. 23:206-215, 1960.

133. Dobkin, A. B. Drugs Which Stimulate Affective Behavior. Anesthesia 15:273-279, 1961.

134. Oberdorf, A. and H. J. Meyer. On the Pharmacology of Megimid. Arch. exp. Path. Pharmak. 238:128-129, 1960.

135. Larsen, V. The General Pharmacology of Benzilic Acid Diethylaminoester Hydrochloride (Benactyzine NFN, Suavitil, Parasan). Acta pharmacol. (Kbh.) 11:405-420, 1955.

136. Farquharson, M. E. and R. G. Johnston. Antagonism of the Effects of Tremorine by Tropine Derivatives. Brit. J. Pharmacol. 14: 559-566, 1960.

137. Boissier, J. R., et al. A New Simple Method for Exploring "Tranquilizing" Action: the Chimney Test. Med. Exptl. 3:81-84, 1960.

138. Bonta, I. L. New Application of the Motility Test in Screening Tranquilizing Drugs. Acta physiol. pharmacol. neerl. 7:519-522, 1958.

139. McColl, J. D. and W. B. Rice. Antagonism of Tremorine by Benactyzine and Dioxolane Analogs. Toxicol. appl. Pharmacol. 4:263-268, 1962.

140. Chen, G. The Anti-Tremorine Effect of Some Drugs as Determined by Haffner's Method of Testing Analgesia in Mice. J. Pharmacol. exp. Ther. 124:73-76, 1958.

141. Denisenko, P. P. Potentiation of Hypnotics and Anesthetics by Central Cholinolytics. Bull. Exp. Biol. Med. 49:593-597, 1960.

142. Frommel, E., et al. On the Differential Pharmacodynamics of Thymoanaleptics and Some "Neuroleptic" Substances in Animal Experimentation. Thérapie 15:1175-1198, 1960.

143. Navarro, M. G. Conditioned Emotional Responses and Psychotropic Drugs. Acta physiol. lat.-amer. 10:122-128, 1960.

144. Hanson, H. M. and D. A. Brodie. Use of the Restrained Rat Technique for Study of the Antiulcer Effect of Drugs. J. appl. Physiol. 15:291-294, 1960.

145. Sacra, P. et al. A Cat and Mouse Test for Studying Changes in Conflict Behavior. Canad. J. Biochem. 35:1151-1152, 1957.

146. Rose, C. L., et al. Toxicity of 3, 3'-Methylenebis (4-Hydroxycoumarin). Proc. Soc. exp. Biol. (N. Y.) 50:228-232, 1942.

147. Lupton, A. M. The Effect of Perfusion through the Isolated Liver on the Prothrombin Activity of Blood from Normal and Dicumarol Treated Rats. J. Pharmacol. exp. Ther. 89: 306-312, 1947.

148. Boura, A. L. A. and A. F. Green. The Actions of Bretylium: Adrenergic Neurone Blocking and Other Effects. Brit. J. Pharmacol. 14:536-548, 1959.

149. Burroughs Wellcome & Co. (U.S.A.), Inc. Personal Communication.

150. Bhagat, B. and F. E. Shideman. Mechanism of the Positive Inotropic Responses to Bretylium and Guanethidine. Brit. J. Pharmacol. 20:56-62, 1963.

151. Green, A. F. and M. F. Sim. Diuresis in Rats: Effects of Sympathomimetic and Sympathetic Blocking Agents. Brit. J. Pharmacol. 17:237-242, 1960.

152. Ryd, G. Protective Effect of Bretylium on Noradrenaline Stores in Organs. Acta physiol. scand. 56:90-93, 1962.

153. Matsumoto, C. and A. Horita. Antagonism of Bretylium by Sumpathomimetic Amines. Nature 195:1212-1213, 1962.

154. Mantegazza, P., et al. The Peripheral Action of Hexamethonium and of Pentolinium. Brit. J. Pharmacol. 13:480-484, 1958.

155. Gessner, P. K. The Relationship between the Metabolic Fate and Pharmacological Action of Serotonin, Bufotenine and Psilocybin. J. Pharmacol. exp. Ther. 130:126-133, 1960.

156. Marczynski, T. and J. Vetulani. Further Investigations on the Pharmacological Properties of 5-Methoxy-N-Methyltryptamine. Diss. pharm. (Krakow) 12:67-84, 1960.

157. Monnier, M. and P. Krupp. Electrophysiological Action of Central Nervous System Stimulants. I. The Adrenergic, Cholinergic and Neurohumoral Serotonic Systems. Arch. int. Pharmacodyn. 127:337-360, 1960.

158. Bunag, R. D. and E. J. Walaszek. Differential Antagonism by RAS-Phenol of Responses to the Indolealkylamines. J. Pharmacol. exp. Ther. 136: 59-67, 1962.

159. Beck, R., et al. Stimulatory Effect of Psychotropic Drugs Demonstrated by Quantitative EEG. Pharmacologist 5:238, 1963.

160. Himwich, W. A. and E. Costa. Behavioral Changes Associated with Changes in Concentrations of Brain Serotonin. Fed. Proc. 19: 838-845, 1960.

161. Chen, B. M. and J. K. Weston. The Analgesic and Anesthetic Effect of 1-(1-Phenylcyclohexyl) Piperidine · HCl on the Monkeys. Anesth. Analg. Curr. Res. 39:132-137, 1960.

162. Molitor, H. The Use of Bulbocapnine in Pre-Anesthetic Medication. J. Pharmacol. exp. Ther. 56:85-96, 1936.

163. Grieg, M. E., et al. Bulbocapnine Catatonia in Mice. Fed. Proc. 17:373, 1958.

164. Zetler, G., et al. Pharmacological Properties of Antidepressive Drugs. Arch. exp. Path. Pharmakol. 238:486-501, 1960.

165. Glow, P. H. The Antagonism of Methyl Phenidate and Iproniazid to Bulbocapnine Catatonia in the Rat. Aust. J. exp. Biol. med. Sci. 40:499-504, 1962.

166. Farris, E. J. and J. Q. Griffith, Jr. The Rat in Laboratory Investigation. J. B. Lippincott Co., Philadelphia, 1949.

167. Walaszek, E. J. and J. E. Chapman. Bulbocapnine: An Adrenergic and Serotonin Blocking Agent. J. Pharmacol. exp. Ther. 137: 285-290, 1962.

168. Walaszek, E. J. and J. E. Chapman. Bulbocapnine: An Adrenergic and Serotonin Blocking Agent. Fed. Proc. 20:314, 1961.

169. Gantt, W. H. Cardiac Conditioning. Trans. 4th Res. Conf. Chemotherap. in Psychiat., Vet. Admin. 4:57-73, 1960.

170. Buchman, E. F. and C. P. Richter. Abolition of Bulbocapnine Catatonia by Cocaine. Arch. Neurol. Psychiat. (Chic.) 29:499, 1933.

171. Boura, A. and A. Green. Adrenergic Neurone Blockade and Other Acute Effects Caused by N-Benzyl-N'N"-Dimethylguanidine and its Ortho-Chloro Derivative. Brit. J. Pharmacol. 20:36-55, 1963.

172. Scott, C. C. and K. K. Chen. Comparison of the Action of 1-Ethyl Theobromine and Caffeine in Animals and Man. J. Pharmacol. exp. Ther. 82:89-97, 1944.

173. Funderburk, W. H., et al. EEG and Biochemical Findings with MAO Inhibitors. Ann. N.Y. Acad. Sci. 96:289-302, 1962.

174. Holm, T., et al. Pharmacology of a Series of Nuclear Substituted Phenyl-Tertiary-Butylamines with Particular Reference to Anorexi-

genic and Central Stimulating Properties. Acta Pharmacol. Toxicol. 17:121-136, 1960.

175. Akiyama, T. Studies on Whirling Syndromes Caused by Iminodipropionitrile. II. The Effect of Several Drugs on the Activity and Light Reaction of Circling Mice. Nippon Yakurigaku Zasshi 56:473-486, 1960.

176. Tripod, J., et al. Characterization of Central Effects of Serpasil (Reserpin, a New Alkaloid of Rauwolfia Serpentina B.) and of their Antagonistic Reactions. Arch. int. Pharmacodyn. 96:406-425, 1954.

177. Dews, P. B. The Measurement of the Influence of Drugs on Voluntary Activity in Mice. Brit. J. Pharmacol. 8:46, 1953.

178. Kreitmair, H. Antagonism between Barbiturates and Convulsants. Arch. exp. Path. Pharmakol. 187:607-616, 1937.

179. Nelson, F. New Apparatus for Experimental Methods Using Psychoactive Substances. Wiss. Z. Friedrich-Schiller-Univ. Jena, Math.-Naturwiss. Reihe 9:549-553, 1960.

180. Scott, C. C., et al. Further Study of Some 1-Substituted Theobromine Compounds. J. Pharmacol. exp. Ther. 86:113-119, 1946.

181. Verhave, T., et al. Effects of Various Drugs on Escape and Avoidance Behavior. Progr. Neurobiol. 3:267-279, 1958.

182. Salant, W. and J. B. Rieger. The Toxicity of Caffein. J. Pharmacol. exp. Ther. 1:572-574, 1910.

183. Sollmann, T. and J. B. Pilcher. The Actions of Caffein on the Mammalian Circulation. I. The Persistent Effects of Caffein on the Circulation. J. Pharmacol. exp. Ther. 3:19-92, 1911.

184. Schallek, W. and A. Kuehn. Effects of Drugs on Spontaneous and Activated EEG of Cat. Arch. int. Pharmacodyn. 120:319-333, 1959.

185. Malis, J. L., et al. Drug Effects on the Behavior of Self Stimulation in Monkeys. Fed. Proc. 19:23, 1960.

186. Cole, V. V., et al. The Toxicity of Strontium and Calcium. J. Pharmacol. exp. Ther. 71:1-5, 1941.

187. Ulrich, J. L. and V. A. Shternov. The Comparative Action of Hypertonic Solutions of the Chlorates and Chlorides of Potassium, Sodium, Calcium and Magnesium. J. Pharmacol. exp. Ther. 35:441-448, 1929.

188. Main, R. J. Mineral Salts as Factors in Urinary Prolan Concentrates. Endocrinology 24:523-525, 1939.

189. La Barre, J. Pharmacological Properties of Carbamyl-β-Methylcholine. I. Effects on Blood Pressure and Pancreas. Arch. int. Pharmacodyn. 106:245-259, 1956.

190. Kreitmair, H. A New Class of Cholinester. Arch. exp. Path. Pharmakol. 164:346-356, 1932.

191. O'Dell, T. B. Experimental Parameters in the Evaluation of Analgesics. Arch. int. Pharmacodyn. 134:154-174, 1961.

192. Frommel, E., et al. Analgesic Potency of Chlorpromazine in Comparison with Morphine and So-Called Morphinic Compounds. Helv. physiol. pharmacol. Acta 18:C24, 1960.

193. Castillo, J. del and T. E. Nelson, Jr. The Mode of Action of Carisoprodol. Ann. N.Y. Acad. Sci. 86:1960.

194. Franklin, K. J. The Pharmacology of Some Compounds Allied to Chloral and to Urethane. J. Pharmacol. exp. Ther. 42:1-7, 1931.

195. Führer, H. Contributions to Comparative Pharmacology. Arch. exp. Path. Pharmakol. 166:437-471, 1932.

196. Gros, O. and H. T. A. Haas. The Antagonism of Narcotics against Cardiazol. Arch. exp. Path. Pharmakol. 192:348-362, 1936.

197. Lehman, G. and P. K. Knoeffel. Trichlorethanol, Tribromethanol, Chloral Hydrate and Bromal Hydrate. J. Pharmacol. exp. Ther. 63:453-465, 1938.

198. Lewin, R. Scopolamine—Chloralhydrate Narcosis. Z. exp. Path. Ther. 18:61-66, 1916.

199. Lendle, L. A Contribution to the General Pharmacology of Narcosis: On the Narcotic Latitudes. Arch. exp. Path. Pharmakol. 132:214-245, 1928.

200. Wolf, A. and E. F. von Haxthausen. Toward the Analysis of the Effects of Some Centrally-Acting Sedative Substances. Arzneimittel-Forsch. 10:50-52, 1960.

BIBLIOGRAPHY

201. Sollmann, T. A Comparative Study of the Dosage and Effects of Chloral Hydrate, Isopral and Bromural on Cats. J. Am. med. Assoc. 51:492, 1908.

202. Sigg, E. B. et al. The Influence of Some Nonbarbiturate Depressants on Central Polysynaptic Mechanisms. Arch. int. Pharmacodyn. 116:450-463, 1958.

203. Adams, W. D. The Comparative Toxicity of Chloral Alcoholate and Chloral Hydrate. J. Pharmacol. exp. Ther. 78:340-345, 1943.

204. Brown, B. B. CNS Drug Actions and Interaction in Mice. Arch. int. Pharmacodyn. 128: 391-414, 1960.

205. Dybing, O. and F. Dybing. Antagonism between Chloralose and Metrazole. Arch. exp. Path. Pharmakol. 199:435-437, 1942.

206. Heffter, A. Chloralglucose and its Action. Berl. klin. Wschr. 20:475, 1893.

207. Hanroit, M. M. and C. Richet. The Chloraloses. Arch. int. Pharmacodyn. 3:191-211, 1897.

208. Elliott, K. A. C. and F. Hobbigero. Gamma Aminobutyric Acid: Circulatory and Respiratory Effects in Different Species; Re-investigation of the Anti-Strychnine Action in Mice. J. Physiol. (Lond.) 146:70-84, 1959.

209. Daly, M. de B. and C. P. Luck. The Effects of Adrenaline and Noradrenalin on Pulmonary Haemodynamics with Special Reference to the Role of Reflexes from the Carotid Sinus Baroreceptors. J. Physiol. (Lond.) 145:108-123, 1959.

210. Hoffman-La Roche, Inc. Personal Communication.

211. Randall, L. O., et al. The Psychosedative Properties of Methaminodiazepoxide. J. Pharmacol. exp. Ther. 129:163-171, 1960.

212. Gershon, S. and W. J. Lang. A Psycho-Pharmacological Study of Some Indole Alkaloids. Arch. int. Pharmacodyn. 135:31-56, 1962.

213. Zbinder, G., et al. Experimental and Clinical Toxicology of Chlordiazepoxide (Librium). Toxicol. appl. Pharmacol. 3:619-637, 1961.

214. Stone, C. A., et al. Ganglionic Blocking Properties of 3-Methylamino-Isocomphane Hydrochloride (Mecamylamine); a Secondary Amine. J. Pharmacol. exp. Ther. 117:169-183, 1956.

215. Plummer, A. J., et al. Ganglionic Blockade by a New Bisquaternary Series Including Chlorisondamine Dimethochloride. J. Pharmacol. exp. Ther. 115:172-184, 1955.

216. Maxwell, R. A., et al. Factors Affecting the Blood Pressure Response of Mammals to the Ganglionic Blocking Agent, Chlorisondamine Chloride. J. Pharmacol. exp. Ther. 123:238-246, 1958.

217. Nickerson, M. and G. M. Nomaguchi. Adrenergic Blocking Action of Phenoxyethyl Analogues of Dibenzamine. J. Pharmacol. exp. Ther. 101:379-396, 1951.

218. Garattini, S. The Pressor Effect of Reserpine after Monoamine-Oxidase Inhibitors. Med. exp. (Basel) 2:252-259, 1960.

219. Raab, W. and R. J. Humphreys. Protective Effect of Adrenolytic Drugs Against Fatal Myocardial Epinephrine Concentrations. J. Pharmacol. exp. Ther. 88:268-276, 1946.

220. Harvey, S. C., et al. Blockade of Epinephrine-Induced Hyperglycemia. J. Pharmacol. exp. Ther. 104:363-376, 1952.

221. Labelle, A. and R. Tislow. Studies on Prophenpyridamine (Timeton) and Chlorprophenpyridamine (Chlortrimeton). J. Pharmacol. exp. Ther. 113:72-88, 1955.

222. Roth, F. E. and W. M. Govier. Comparative Pharmacology of Chlorpheniramine (Chlor-Trimeton) and its Optical Isomers. J. Pharmacol. exp. Ther. 124:347-349, 1958.

223. Schering Corporation. Personal Communication.

224. Hanson, H. M., et al. Drug Modification of Runway Behavior of Mice as Influenced by an Aversive Stimulus. Fed. Proc. 17:375, 1958.

225. Burton, R. M., et al. Interaction of Nicotinamide with Reserpine and Chlorpromazine. II. Some Effects on the Central Nervous System of the Mouse. Arch. int. Pharmacodyn. 128:253-259, 1960.

226. Fink, G. B. and E. Swinyard. Modification of Maximal Audiogenic and Electroshock Seizures in Mice by Psychopharmacologic Drugs. J. Pharmacol. exp. Ther. 127:318-324, 1959.

227. Boissier, J. R. Neuroleptics and Experimental Catatonia. Thérapie 15:73-77, 1960.

228. Irwin, S. Symposia on the Use of Tranquilizers in Veterinary Practice. Schering Corp., Bloomfield, N. J., 1958.

229. Weiss, B. and V. G. Laties. Effects of Amphetamine, Chlorpromazine and Pentobarbital on Behavioral Thermoregulation. J. Pharmacol. exp. Ther. 140:1-7, 1963.

230. Ito, S. The Effect of Several Tranquilizers on the Conditioned Avoidance Reaction of White Rats. Nippon Yakurigaku Zasshi 56: 377-386, 1960.

231. Ishikawa, S. A Pharmacological Study of Phenothiazine Derivatives. Nippon Yakurigaku Zasshi 56:498-513, 1960.

232. Jewett, R. and S. Norton. Drug Effects on Behavior of the Rat under Chronic Isolation. Pharmacologist 5:240, 1963.

233. Buchel, L. and J. Levy. Contribution to the Study of the Mechanism of Sedative Action of Reserpine. J. Physiol. (Paris) 52:727-733, 1960.

234. Yagi, K., et al. The Effect of Flavin Adenine Dinucleotide on the Electroencephalogram Modified by Chlorpromazine. J. Neurochem. 5:304-306, 1960.

235. Domenjoz, R. and W. Theobald. The Pharmacology of Tofranil (N-(3-Dimethyl-amino-propyl)-Iminodibenzylhydrochloride). Arch. int. Pharmacodyn. 120:450-489, 1959.

236. Komendantova, M. V. The Meaning of the Ion Component in the Pharmacodynamics of Aminazine. Farmakol. i Toksikol. 23:99-105, 1960.

237. Enge, S. and H. Lechner. An Experimental Contribution to the Mode of Drug Action in Animals. Wien. Z. Nervenheilk. u. Grenzg. 17:309-323, 1960.

238. Barkov, N. K. Analgetic Properties of Phenothiazine Derivatives. Farmakol. i Toksikol. 23:311-315, 1960.

239. Adey, W. R. and C. W. Dunlop. Amygdaloid and Peripheral Influences on Caudate and Pallidal Units in the Cat and Effects of Chlorpromazine. Exp. Neurol. 2:348-363, 1960.

240. Kaada, B. R. and H. Bruland. Blocking of the Cortically Induced Behavioral Attention (Orienting) Response by Chlorpromazine. Psychopharmacologia 1:372-388, 1960.

241. Feldman, S. and M. Eliakim. Observations on the Mechanism of Blood Pressure Changes Following Chlorpromazine Administration in the Cat. Arch. int. Pharmacodyn. 141:340-356, 1958.

242. Leutova, F. A. The Problem of the Mechanism of the Action of Aminazine and Physical Cooling on the Therapeutic Reflexes. Zh. Nevropat. Psikhiat. 60:210-219, 1960.

243. Polezhayev, E. F. Action of Aminazine and Adrenaline in Small Doses on the Formation of Cortical Coordination. Zh. Nevropat. Psikhiat. 60:568-576, 1960.

244. Agangants, E. K. Effects of Chlorpromazine and Ethylene on Conditioned Reflexes in Dogs. Pavlov J. higher nerv. Activ. 10:899-908, 1960.

245. Khananashbili, M. M. The Mechanism of Action of Chlorpromazine on Higher Nervous Activity. Farmakol. i Toksikol. 23:295-299, 1960.

246. Fuller, J. L., et al. Effects of Chlorpromazine upon Psychological Development in the Puppy. Psychopharmacologia 1:393-407, 1960.

247. Domino, E. F. and S. Ueki. An Analysis of the Electrical Burst Phenomenon in Some Rhinencephalic Structures of the Dog and Monkey. Electroenceph. clin. Neurophysiol. 12:635-648, 1960.

248. Weitzman, E. and G. Ross. Behavioral Method for Study of Pain Perception in Monkeys. Neurology (Minneap.) 12:264-272, 1962.

249. Browning, H. C., et al. Weights of Thymus and Seminal Vesicle in Castrate Mice as Altered by Intraperitoneal and Subcutaneous Injections of Testerone. Tox. Rep. Biol. Med. 19:753-760, 1961.

250. Stone, G. C., et al. Behavioral and Pharmacological Studies of Thiopropazate, a Potent Tranquilizing Agent. Arch. int. Pharmacodyn. 127:85-103, 1960.

251. Chen, G. and B. Bohner. A Study of Certain CNS Depressants. Arch. int. Pharmacodyn. 125:1-20, 1960.

252. Tanaka, K. and Y. Kawasaki. A Group of

Compounds Possessing Anticonvulsant Activity in the Maximal Electroshock Seizure Test. Jap. J. Pharmacol. 6:115-121, 1957.

253. Luduena, F. P., et al. Effect of Adrenergic Blockers and Related Compounds on the Toxicity of Epinephrine in Rats. Arch. int. Pharmacodyn. 122:111-122, 1959.

254. Busch, V. G., et al. Electrophysiological Analysis of the Action of Hemoleptic and Tranquilizing Substances (Phenothiazine, Meprobamate) on the Spinal Motor System. Arzneimittel-Forsch. 10:217-223, 1960.

255. Piala, J. J., et al. Pharmacology of Benzhydroflumethazide (Naturetin). J. Pharmacol. exp. Ther. 134:273-280, 1961.

256. Bacharach, A. L. The Effect of Ingested Vitamin E (Tocopherol) on Vitamin A Storage in the Liver of the Albino Rat. Quart. J. Pharm. 14:138-149, 1940.

257. Fromherz, K. Larocain, a New Local Anesthetic. Arch. exp. Path. Pharmakol. 158:368-380, 1930.

258. Hooper, C. W. and E. Becker. A Quantitative Comparison of Toxicity of Alkamine Esters of Aromatic Acids Used as Local Anesthetics. Am. J. Physiol. 68:120, 1924.

259. Rose, C. L., et al. Studies in the Pharmacology of Local Anesthetics. III. Comparison of Gamma-(2-Methyl Piperidine) Propyl Benzoate Hydrochloride with Cocaine and Procaine on Experimental Animals. J. Lab. clin. Med. 15:731-735, 1930.

260. Eicholtz, F. and C. Hoppe. The Convulsive Action of Local Anesthetics and the Effect of Mineral Salts and Adrenaline. Arch. exp. Path. Pharmakol. 173:687-696, 1933.

261. Brodie, B. B. Comparison of Central Actions of Cocaine and LSD. Fed. Proc. 16: 284, 1957.

262. Bogdanski, D. and S. Spector. Comparison of Central Actions of Cocaine and LSD. Fed. Proc. 16:284, 1957.

263. Wingard, C. and R. S. Teague. Potentiation of the Pressor Response to Epinephrine and Sympathomimetic Aldehydes. Arch. int. Pharmacodyn. 116:54-64, 1958.

264. Chen, G. and B. Bohner. The Anti-Reserpine Effects of Certain Centrally-Acting Agents. J. Pharmacol. exp. Ther. 131:179-184, 1961.

265. MacMillan, W. H. A Hypothesis Concerning the Effect of Cocaine on the Action of Sympathomimetic Amines. Brit. J. Pharmacol. 14:385-391, 1959.

266. Gurd, M. R. The Physiological Action of Dihydroxyphenylethylamine and Sympatol. Quart. J. and Year Book of Pharm. 10:188-211, 1937.

267. Kissel, J. W., et al. The Pharmacology of Prodilidine Hydrochloride, a New Analgetic Agent. J. Pharmacol. exp. Ther. 134:332-340, 1961.

268. Poe, C. F. and J. G. Strong. The Toxicity of Certain Compounds for Male and Female Rats of Different Ages. J. Pharmacol. exp. Ther. 58:239-242, 1936.

269. Ercoli, N. and M. N. Lewis. Studies on Analgesics. J. Pharmacol. exp. Ther. 84: 301-317, 1945.

270. Eddy, N. B. and M. Sumwalt. Studies of Morphine, Codeine and their Derivatives. XV. 2, 4-Dinitrophenylmorphine. J. Pharmacol. exp. Ther. 67:127-141, 1939.

271. O'Dell, T. B., et al. Pharmacology of a Series of New 2-Substituted Pyridine Derivatives with Emphasis on their Analgesic and Interneuronal Blocking Properties. J. Pharmacol. exp. Ther. 128:65-74, 1960.

272. Goldberg, B., et al. Colchicine Derivatives. I. Toxicity in Mice and Effects on Mouse Sarcoma 180. Cancer 3:124-129, 1950.

273. Streicher, E. Toxicity of Colchicine, Di-Isopropyl Fluorophosphate, Intocostrin, and Potassium Cyanide in Mice at 4° C. Proc. Soc. exp. Biol. (N. Y.) 76:536-538, 1951.

274. Sollmann, T. A Manual of Pharmacology and its Application to Therapeutics and Toxicology. W. B. Saunders Co. (7th ed.), Philadelphia, 1948.

275. Ferguson, F. C., Jr. Colchicine. I. General Pharmacology. J. Pharmacol. exp. Ther. 106: 261-270, 1952.

276. Santav, F., et al. Mitolytic Action and Toxicity of New Substances Isolated from Colchicine. Arch. int. Pharmacodyn. 84:257-268, 1950.

277. Maurel, M. Influence of Route of Administration on the Production of Colchicine-Diarrhea in the Rabbit. C. R. Soc. Biol. (Paris) 67:768-769, 1909.

278. Dixon, W. E. and W. Malden. Colchicine with Special Reference to its Mode of Action and Effect on Bone Marrow. J. Physiol. (Lond.) 37:50-76, 1908.

279. Fernandez, E. and A. Cerletti. Studies on the Hypotensive Mechanism of Protoveratrine. Arch. int. Pharmacodyn. 100:425-435, 1955.

280. Castillo, J. C. and E. J. de Beer. The Neuromuscular Blocking Action of Succinylcholine (Diacetylcholine). J. Pharmacol. exp. Ther. 99:458-464, 1950.

281. Bovet, D., et al. Studies on Synthetic Curare-Like Poisons. Arch. int. Pharmacodyn. 88:1-50, 1951.

282. Walton, R. P., et al. Inotropic Activity of Catechol Isomers and a Series of Related Compounds. J. Pharmacol. exp. Ther. 125: 202-207, 1959.

283. Paton, W. D. M. and E. J. Zamis. Clinical Potentialities of Certain Bisquaternary Salts Causing Neuromuscular and Ganglionic Block. Nature (Lond.) 162:810, 1948.

284. Setniker, I., et al. Amino-Methylchromes, Brain Stem Stimulants and Pentobarbital Antagonists. J. Pharmacol. exp. Ther. 128: 176-181, 1960.

285. Day, M. and M. Rand. Evidence for a Competitive Antagonism of Guanethidine by Dexamphetamine. Brit. J. Pharmacol. 20:17-28, 1963.

286. Buchel, L., et al. A Contribution to the Study of the Effects of Hydrazine-2-Phenyl-3-Propane (PIH) on the Central Nervous System, Compared with Those of 1-Isonicotinyl-2-Isopropylhydrazide (Iproniazid). IV. Influence on Analgesia Induced by 1-Methadone. Agressologie 1:389-396, 1960.

287. Hamilton, C. L. Effects of LSD-25 and Amphetamine on a Running Response in the Rat. Arch. gen. Psychiat. 2:104-109, 1960.

288. Sergio, C. Effects of Bulbocapnine in Some Decorticated Rabbits. Riv. Neurobiol. 6:51-53, 1960.

289. Jarvik, M. E. and S. Chorover. Impairment by Lysergic Acid Diethylamide of Accuracy in Performance of a Delayed Alternation Test in Monkeys. Psychopharmacologia 1: 221-230, 1960.

290. Kleindorf, G. B. and J. T. Halsey. A Study of the Relative Efficiency as "Basal Anesthetics" of Avertin, Amytal, Chloral, Dial, and Isopropyl Allyl Barbituric Acid. J. Pharmacol. exp. Ther. 43:449-456, 1931.

291. Peterson, I. and E. Bohm. Differences in Sensitivity to Dial of Motor Effects Elicited by Stimulation of Fore- and Hindlimb Areas of the Cat's Motor Cortex. Acta physiol. scand. 29:143-146, 1953.

292. Schneider, J. A. and F. F. Yonkman. Action of Serotonin (5-Hydroxytryptamine) on Vagal Afferent Impulses in the Cat. Am. J. Physiol. 174:127-134, 1953.

293. O'Leary, J. F. Cardiovascular Actions of 1, 4-Bis (1, 4-Benzodioxan-2-yl-Methyl) Piperazine (McN-181, Dibozane), a New Adrenergic Blocking Agent. Fed. Proc. 12:355, 1953.

294. Yelnosky, L. and L. C. Mortimer. A Brief Study of the Sympathomimetic Cardiovascular Effects of Bretylium. Arch. int. Pharmacodyn. 130:200-206, 1961.

295. Rapela, C. E. and H. D. Green. Adrenergic Blockade by Dibozane. J. Pharmacol. exp. Ther. 132:29-41, 1961.

296. Powell, C. E. and I. H. Slater. Blocking of Inhibitory Adrenergic Receptors by a Dichloro Analog of Isoproterenol. J. Pharmacol. exp. Ther. 122:480-488, 1958.

297. Eli Lilly and Company. Personal Communication.

298. Goldstein, L. and C. Munoz. Influence of Adrenergic Stimulant and Blocking Drugs on Cerebral Electrical Activity in Curarized Animals. J. Pharmacol. exp. Ther. 132:345-353, 1961.

299. Levy, B. Adrenergic Blockade Produced by the Dichloro Analogs of Epinephrine, Arterenol and Isoproterenol. J. Pharmacol. exp. Ther. 127:150-156, 1959.

300. Ahlquist, R. P. and B. Levy. Adrenergic Receptive Mechanism of Canine Ileum. J. Pharmacol. exp. Ther. 127:146-149, 1959.

301. Hall, W. J. The Action of Tyramine on the

Dog Isolated Atrium. Brit. J. Pharmacol. 20: 245-253, 1963.

302. Fleming, W. W. and D. F. Hawkins. The Actions of Dichloroisoproternol in the Dog Heart-Lung Preparation and Isolated Guinea Pig Atrium. J. Pharmacol. exp. Ther. 129: 1-10, 1960.

303. Lendle, L. Digitalis Substances and Related Glycosides Working on the Heart (Digitaloids). Heffter's Hdb. E. 1:11-265, 1935.

304. Röthlin, E. On the Pharmacology of the Hydrated Natural Mother Seed Alkaloids. Helv. physiol. pharmacol. Acta 2:C48, 1944.

305. Naranjo, P. and E. B. de Naranjo. Pressor Effect of Histamine in the Rabbit. J. Pharmacol. exp. Ther. 123:16-21, 1958.

306. West, T. C. and J. M. Dille. Reversal of Depressor Effect of TEA. J. Pharmacol. exp. Ther. 108:233-239, 1953.

307. Buchwald, M. E. and G. S. Eadie. The Toxicology of Dilaudid Injected Intravenously into Mice. J. Pharmacol. exp. Ther. 71:197-202, 1941.

308. Eddy, N. B. and J. G. Reid. Studies of Morphine, Codeine and their Derivatives. VII. Dihydromorphine (Paramorphan), Dihydromorphinone (Dilaudid), and Dihydrocodeinone (Dicodide). J. Pharmacol. exp. Ther. 52: 468-493, 1934.

309. Friebel, H. and C. Reichle. Analgesia and Analgesia-Enhancing Effects of Chlorpromazine. Arch. exp. Path. Pharmakol. 226:551-573, 1955.

310. Eddy, N. B. and H. A. Howes. Studies of Morphine, Codeine and their Derivatives. J. Pharmacol. exp. Ther. 53:430-439, 1935.

311. Horton, R. G., et al. The Acute Toxicity of Di-Isopropyl Fluorophosphate. J. Pharmacol. exp. Ther. 87:414-429, 1946.

312. Koelle, G. B. and A. Gilman. The Relationship between Cholinesterase Inhibition and the Pharmacological Action of Di-Isopropyl Fluorophosphate (DFP). J. Pharmacol. exp. Ther. 87:421-434, 1946.

313. Cook, D. L., et al. Pharmacology of a New Autonomic Ganglion Blocking Agent, 2, 6-Dimethyl-1, 1-Diethyl Piperidinium Bromide (SC-1950). J. Pharmacol. exp. Ther. 99:435-443, 1950.

314. Chen, G., et al. Pharmacology of 1, 1-Dimethyl-4-Phenylpiperazinium Iodide, A Ganglionic Stimulating Agent. J. Pharmacol. exp. Ther. 103:330-336, 1951.

315. Tainter, M. L. and W. C. Cutting. Miscellaneous Actions of Dinitrophenol. Repeated Administrations, Antidotes, Fatal Doses, Antiseptic Tests and Actions of Some Isomers. J. Pharmacol. exp. Ther. 49:187-208, 1933.

316. Spencer, H. C., et al. Toxicological Studies on Laboratory Animals of Certain Alkyldinitrophenols Used in Agriculture. J. industr. Hyg. 30:10-25, 1948.

317. Tainter, M. L., et al. Metabolic Activity of Compounds Related to Dinitrophenol. J. Pharmacol. exp. Ther. 53:58-66, 1935.

318. Magne, H., et al. Pharmacodynamic Action of the Nitrated Phenols: An Agent Increasing Cellular Oxidations, 2, 4-Dinitrophenol. Ann. physiol. physiochim. biol. 8:1-50, 1932.

319. Tainter, M. L. and W. C. Cutting. Febrile, Respiratory and Some Other Actions of Dinitrophenol. J. Pharmacol. exp. Ther. 48: 410-429, 1933.

320. Way, E. L. and W. C. Herbert. The Effect of Sodium Pentobarbital on the Toxicity of Certain Antihistamines. J. Pharmacol. exp. Ther. 104:115-121, 1952.

321. Gruhzit, O. M. and R. A. Fisken. A Toxicological Study of Two Histamine Antagonists of the Benzhydryl Alkamine Ether Group. J. Pharmacol. exp. Ther. 89:227-233, 1947.

322. De Salva, S. and R. Evans. Anticonvulsive Character of Styramate and Other Depressant Drugs. Toxicol. appl. Pharmacol. 2:397-402, 1960.

323. Chen, G. and B. Bohner. A Study of Central Nervous System Stimulants. J. Pharmacol. exp. Ther. 123:212-215, 1958.

324. Loew, E. R. Pharmacology of Antihistamine Compounds. Physiol. Rev. 27:542-573, 1947.

325. Sachs, B. A. The Toxicity of Benadryl: Report of a Case and Review of the Literature. Ann. intern. Med. 29:135-144, 1948.

326. De Salva, S. and R. Evans. Continuous Intravenous Infusion of Strychnine in Rats: II. Antagonism by Various Drugs. Arch. int. Pharmacodyn. 125:355-361, 1960.

327. Blaschko, H. and T. L. Chrusciel. The Decarboxylation of Amino Acids Related to Tyrosine and their Awakening Action in Reserpine-Treated Mice. J. Physiol. (Lond.) 151:272-284, 1960.

328. Page, I. H. and R. Reed. Hypertensive Effect of L-Dopa and Related Compounds in the Rat. Am. J. Physiol. 143:122-125, 1945.

329. Kato, R. Effects of Pre-Electroshock Treatment on the Duration of Tranquilizer Effect, and on the Contents of Brain Serotonin. Nippon Yakurigaku Zasshi 56:1046-1053, 1960.

330. Burn, J. H. and M. J. Rand. The Depressor Action of Dopamine and Adrenaline. Brit. J. Pharmacol. 13:471-479, 1958.

331. Costa, E., et al. Brain Concentration of Biogenic Amines and EEG Patterns of Rabbits. J. Pharmacol. exp. Ther. 130:81-88, 1960.

332. Rowe, L. W. The Comparative Pharmacologic Action of Ephedrine and Adrenalin. J. Am. pharm. Ass. 16:912-918, 1927.

333. Chen, K. K. and C. F. Schmidt. The Action and Clinical Use of Ephedrine. J. Amer. med. Ass. 87:836-842, 1926.

334. Chen, K. K. The Acute Toxicity of Ephedrine. J. Pharmacol. exp. Ther. 27:61-76, 1926.

335. Hauschild, F. On the Pharmacology of 1-Phenyl-2-Methylaminopropane (Pervitin). Arch. exp. Path. Pharm. 191:465-481, 1939.

336. Watson, R. H. J. Constitutional Differences between Two Strains of Rats with Different Behavioral Characteristics. Advanc. Psychosomatic Med. 1:160-165, 1960.

337. Grishina, V. M. Antihypnotic Action of Ephedrine. Farmakol. i Toksikol. 23:287-295, 1960.

338. Axelrod, J. and R. Tomchick. Increased Rate of Metabolism of Epinephrine and Norepinephrine by Sympathomimetic Amines. J. Pharmacol. exp. Ther. 130:367-369, 1960.

339. Burn, J. H. and M. J. Rand. The Action of Sympathetic Amines in Animals Treated with Reserpine. J. Physiol. (Lond.) 144:314-336, 1958.

340. Lands, A. M., et al. The Pharmacology of N-Alkyl Homologues of Epinephrine. J. Pharmacol. exp. Ther. 90:110-119, 1947.

341. Bovet, D. and G. Bovet-Nitti. Medications of the Autonomic Nervous System. S. Karger, New York, 1948.

342. Levy, J. and E. Michel-Ber. A Hypothesis about the Mechanisms of Action of Monamine Oxidase Inhibitors at the Central Nervous System Level. C. R. Acad. Sci. (Paris) 250: 415-417, 1960.

343. Raab, W. and R. J. Humphreys. Protective Effect of Adrenolytic Drugs against Fatal Myocardial Epinephrine Concentrations. J. Pharmacol. exp. Ther. 88:268-276, 1946.

344. Smythies, J. R. and C. K. Levy. The Comparative Pharmacology of Some Mescaline Analogues. J. ment. Sci. 106:531-536, 1960.

345. Savoldi, F., et al. Action of a Water-Soluble Derivative of Theobromine on the Cerebral Circulation and Cortical Electrical Activity of the Rabbit. Arch. ital. Sci. farmacol. 10: 231-240, 1960.

346. Spector, W. S. Handbook of Toxicology. Vol. I. WADC Technical Report 55-16, 1955.

347. Kostos, V. J. and J. J. Kocsis. Tissue Serotonin (5-HT) Levels in Colchicine Treated Rats and Rabbits. Pharmacologist 5:247, 1963.

348. Röthlin, E. Investigation of Ergotamine, a Specific Alkaloid of Ergot. Arch. int. Pharmacodyn. 27:459-479, 1923.

349. Röthlin, E. The Pharmacological Properties of a New Alkaloid of Ergot, Ergobasine. C. R. Soc. Biol. (Paris) 119:1302-1304, 1935.

350. Laurence, D. R. and R. S. Stacey. Mechanism of the Prevention of Nicotine Convulsions by Hexamethonium and by Adrenaline Blocking Agents. Brit. J. Pharmacol. 8:62-65, 1953.

351. Barger, G. The Alkaloids of Ergot. Heffter's Hdb. E. 6:84-222, 1938.

352. Sandoz Pharmaceuticals. Personal Communication.

353. Ginzel, K. H. The Effect of d-Lysergic Acid Diethylamide and Other Drugs on the Carotid Sinus Reflex. Brit. J. Pharmacol. 13:250-259, 1958.

354. Mayer, S., et al. The Effect of Adrenergic

Blocking Agents on Some Metabolic Actions of Catecholamines. J. Pharmacol. exp. Ther. 134:18-27, 1961.

355. Graham, G., et al. Influence of Fluoroacetate on Renal Acid Secretion. Fed. Proc. 12:325, 1953.

356. Furchgott, R. F. The Effect of Sodium Fluoroacetate on the Contractility and Metabolism of Intestinal Smooth Muscle. J. Pharmacol. exp. Ther. 99:1-15, 1950.

357. Matthews, R. J. and B. J. Roberts. The Effect of Gamma-Aminobutyric Acid on Synaptic Transmission in Autonomic Ganglia. J. Pharmacol. exp. Ther. 132:19-22, 1961.

358. Rech, R. H. and E. F. Domino. Effects of Gamma-Aminobutyric Acid on Chemically and Electrically Evoked Activity in the Isolated Cerebral Cortex of the Dog. J. Pharmacol. exp. Ther. 130:59-67, 1960.

359. Gulati, O. D. and H. C. Stanton. Some Effects on the Central Nervous System of Gamma-Amino-n-Butyric Acid (GABA) and Certain Related Amino Acids Administered Systemically and Intracerebrally to Mice. J. Pharmacol. exp. Ther. 129:175-185, 1960.

360. Winter, C. A. and J. T. Lehman. Studies on Synthetic Curarizing Agents. J. Pharmacol. exp. Ther. 100:489-501, 1950.

361. Bovet, D., et al. Studies on Synthetic Curare-Like Poisons. Arch. int. Pharmacodyn. 80: 172-188, 1949.

362. Longo, V. G. Effects of Scopolamine and Atropine on Electroencephalographic and Behavioral Reactions Due to Hypothalamic Stimulation. J. Pharmacol. exp. Ther. 116: 198-208, 1956.

363. Maxwell, R. A., et al. Pharmacology of (2(Octahydro-1-Azocinyl)-Ethyl)-Guanidine Sulfate (SU-5864). J. Pharmacol. exp. Ther. 128:22-29, 1960.

364. Bogaert, M., et al. On the Pharmacology of Guanethidine. Arch. int. Pharmacodyn. 134:224-236, 1961.

365. Cass, R. and T. Spriggs. Tissue Amine Levels and Sympathetic Blockade after Guanethidine and Bretylium. Brit. J. Pharmacol. 17:442-450, 1961.

366. Cass, R., et al. Norepinephrine Depletion as a Possible Mechanism of Action of Guanethidine (SU-5864), a New Hypotensive Agent. Proc. Soc. exp. Biol. (N.Y.) 103:871-872, 1960.

367. Dagirmanjian, R. The Effects of Guanethidine on the Noradrenaline Content of the Hypothalamus in the Cat and Rat. J. Pharm. Pharmacol. 15:518-521, 1963.

368. Gunn, J. A. The Pharmacological Action of Harmaline. Trans. Roy. Soc. Edin. 47:245-272, 1909.

369. Ahmed, A. and N. R. W. Taylor. The Analysis of Drug-Induced Tremor in Mice. Brit. J. Pharmacol. 14:350-354, 1959.

370. Pellmont, B. and F. A. Steiner. Influence on a Conditioned Reflex by Drugs with Effects on Monamine Metabolism in the Central Nervous System. Psychiat. et Neurol. (Basel) 140: 216-219, 1960.

371. Spector, S., et al. Evidence for Release of Brain Amines by Reserpine in Presence of Monoamine Oxidase Inhibitors: Implication of Monoamine Oxidase in Norepinephrine Metabolism in Brain. J. Pharmacol. exp. Ther. 130:256-261, 1960.

372. Goldberg, L. I. and A. Sjoerdsma. Effects of Several Monoamine Oxidase Inhibitors on the Cardiovascular Actions of Naturally Occurring Amines in the Dog. J. Pharmacol. exp. Ther. 127:212-218, 1959.

373. Hara, S. and I. Mori. Investigation of Poisons of the Extrapyramidal Paths. II. Pharmacological Contribution to Harmin. Jap. J. Med. Sc. IV Pharm. 7:78-79, 1933.

374. Gunn, J. A. and R. C. MacKeith. The Pharmacological Actions of Harmol. Quart. J. Pharm. 4:33-51, 1931.

375. Lewin, L. Chemistry and Pharmacological Action of Banisteria Caapi Spr. Arch. exp. Path. Pharmakol. 129:133-149, 1928.

376. Goldberg, L. I. and F. M. DeCosta. Selective Depression of Sympathetic Transmission by Intravenous Administration of Iproniazid and Harmine. Proc. Soc. exp. Biol. (N.Y.) 105:223-227, 1960.

377. Marshall, F. N. and J. P. Long. Pharmacologic Studies on Some Compounds Structurally Related to the Hemicholinium HC-3. J. Pharmacol. exp. Ther. 127:236-240, 1959.

378. Kase, Y. and H. L. Borison. Central Respiratory Depressant Effect of "Hemicholinium." Fed. Proc. 16:311, 1957.

379. Zablocka, B. and D. Esplin. Evidence for a Cholinergic Link in "Direct" Spinal Inhibition. Pharmacologist 5:237, 1963.

380. Seifter, J. and A. J. Begany. Studies on the Action of a Synthetic Heparinoid. Am. J. med. Sci. 216:234-235, 1948.

381. Montague, D., et al. Bradykinin: Vascular Relaxant, Cardiac Stimulant. Science 141: 907-908, 1963.

382. Wenke, M. Relation between the Heparin Dose and the Esterolytic Activity Level in the Blood Serum of Rats. Arch. int. Pharmacodyn. 134:417-425, 1961.

383. Gillis, C. N. and C. W. Nash. The Initial Pressor Actions of Bretylium Tosylate and Guanethidine Sulfate and their Relation to Release of Catecholamines. J. Pharmacol. exp. Ther. 134:1-7, 1961.

384. Wolff, R. and J. J. Brignon. A Study of the Serum-Clearing Activity of Several Heparin-Like Substances in vitro. Arch. int. Pharmacodyn. 121:255-267, 1959.

385. Davey, M. J., et al. The Effects of Nialamide on Adrenergic Functions. Brit. J. Pharmacol. 20:121-134, 1963.

386. Salmoiraghi, G. C., et al. Effects of d-Lysergic Acid Diethylamine and its Brom Derivative on Cardiovascular Responses to Serotonin and on Arterial Pressure. J. Pharmacol. exp. Ther. 119:240-247, 1957.

387. Grollman, A. The Effect of Various Hypotensive Agents on the Arterial Blood Pressure of Hypertensive Rats and Dogs. J. Pharmacol. exp. Ther. 14:263-270, 1955.

388. Della Bella, D. and F. Rognoni. Neurovegetative Control of Gastric Motility in the Isolated Nerve-Stomach Preparation of the Rat. J. Pharmacol. exp. Ther. 134:184-189, 1961.

389. Kennedy, W. P. Sodium Salt of C-C-Cyclohexenylmethyl-N-Methyl Barbituric Acid (Evipan) Anaesthesia in Laboratory Animals. J. Pharmacol. exp. Ther. 50:347-353, 1934.

390. Buller, R. H., et al. The Potentiating Effect of 4, 5-Dihydro-6-Methyl-2[2-(4-Pyridyl)-Ethyl]-3-Pyridazinone (U-320) on Hexobarbital Hypnosis. J. Pharmacol. exp. Ther. 134:95-99, 1961.

391. Reinhard, J. F., et al. Pharmacologic Characteristics of 1-(Ortho-Toluoxy)-2, 3-Bis-(2, 2, 2-Trichloro-1 Hydroxyethoxy)-Propane. J. Pharmacol. exp. Ther. 106:444-452, 1952.

392. Bush, M. T., et al. The Metabolic Fate of Evipal (Hexobarbital) and of "Nor-Evipal." J. Pharmacol. exp. Ther. 108:104-111 (1953).

393. Maloney, A. H. and R. Hertz. Sodium N-Methyl-Cyclohexenyl-Methyl-Barbituric Acid (Evipal): Hypnosis, Anesthesia and Toxicity. J. Pharmacol. exp. Ther. 54:77-83, 1935.

394. Werner, H. W., et al. A Comparative Study of Several Ultrashortacting Barbiturates, Nembutal, and Tribromethanol. J. Pharmacol. exp. Ther. 60:189-197, 1937.

395. Shimamoto, K., et al. Peripheral Action of the Ganglion Blocking Agents. Jap. J. Pharmacol. 5:66-76, 1955.

396. Takagi, H. and T. Ban. Effect of Psychotropic Drugs on the Limbic System of the Cat. Jap. J. Pharmacol. 10:7-14, 1960.

397. Lin, T. M., et al. 3-β-Aminoethyl-1, 2, 4-Triazole, a Potent Stimulant of Gastric Secretion. J. Pharmacol. exp. Ther. 134:88-94, 1961.

398. Lands, A. M., et al. The Pharmacological Properties of Three New Antihistaminic Drugs. J. Pharmacol. exp. Ther. 95:45-52, 1949.

399. Schmidt, G. W. and A. Stähelin. Histamine Sensitivity and Anaphylaxis Reaction. Z. Innunitatstorsch. 60:222-238, 1929.

400. Parrot, J. L., et al. Acute Intoxication of the Cobaye through Gastric Administration of Histamine Alone or Associated with Putrescence. 17th Int. Physiol. Cong., 1947: p. 378.

401. Camus, L. Hordenine, the Degree of the Toxic Symptoms of Intoxication. C. R. Acad. Sci. (Paris) 142:110-113, 1906.

402. Barger, G. and H. H. Dale. Chemical Structure and Sympathomimetic Action of Amines. J. Physiol. (Lond.) 41:19-59, 1910.

403. Craver, N. The Activities of 1-Hydrazinophthalazine (Ba-5968), a Hypotensive Agent.

J. Amer. pharm. Ass., sci. Ed. 40:559-564, 1961.

404. Schmitt, H. Adrenolytic, Noradrenolytic and Sympatholytic Action of Dibenzyline (SKF 688A). Arch. int. Pharmacodyn. 109:263-270, 1957.

405. Rocha e Silva, M., et al. Potentiation of Duration of the Vasodilator Effect of Bradykinin by Sympatholytic Drugs and Reserpine. J. Pharmacol. exp. Ther. 128:217-226, 1960.

406. Kuschinsky, G. Investigation of Sympathol, an Adrenergic Compound. Arch. exp. Path. Pharmakol. 156:290-308, 1930.

407. Mancini, M. A. The Pharmacology of the Autonomous System. Boll. Soc. ital. Biol. sper. 4:224-225, 1929.

408. Maxwell, R. A., et al. Concerning a Possible Action of Guanethidine (SU-5864) in Smooth Muscle. J. Pharmacol. exp. Ther. 129:24-30, 1960.

409. Randall, L. O. and G. Lehmann. Analgesic Action of 3-Hydroxy-N-Methyl Morphinan Hydrobromide (Dromoran). J. Pharmacol. exp. Ther. 99:163-170, 1950.

410. Bogdanski, D. F., et al. Pharmacological Studies with the Serotonin Precursor, 5-Hydroxytryptophan. J. Pharmacol. exp. Ther. 122:182-194, 1958.

411. Buchel, L. and J. Levy. Contribution to the Study of the Effects on the Central Nervous System of Monoamine Oxidese Inhibitors, Hydrazine-2-phenyl-3 propane (P. I. H.), Isopropylhydrazide of Isonicotinic Acid (Iproniazid), II. Influence on Potentiation of Experimental Sleep by Reserpine. Anesth. et Analg. 17:313-328, 1960.

412. Anderson, E. G. The Effects of Harmaline and 5-Hydroxytryptamine on Spinal Synaptic Transmission. Pharmacologist 5:238, 1963.

413. Cronhein, G. E. and J. T. Gourzis. Cardiovascular and Behavioral Effects of Serotonin and Related Substances in Dogs without and with Reserpine Premedications. J. Pharmacol. exp. Ther. 130:444-449, 1960.

414. Haas, H. On 3-Piperidino-1-Phenyl-1-Bicycloheptenylpropanol-(1) (Akineton). Second Report. Arch. int. Pharmacodyn. 128:204-238, 1960.

415. Read, G. W., et al. Comparison of Excited Phases after Sedatives and Tranquilizers. Psychopharmacologia 1:346-350, 1960.

416. Hughes, F. W. and E. Kopman. Influence of Pentobarbital, Hydroxyzine, Chlorpromazine, Reserpine, and Meprobamate on Choice-Discrimination Behavior in the Rat. Arch. int. Pharmacodyn. 126:158-170, 1960.

417. Hotovy, R. and J. Kopff-Walter. On the Pharmacological Properties of Perphenazinsulfoxide. Arzneimittel-Forsch. 10:638-650, 1960.

418. Lynes, T. E. and F. M. Berger. Some Pharmacological Properties of Hydroxyzine (1-(p-Chlorobenzhydryl-4-(2-(2-Hydroxyethoxy)-ethyl) Diethylenediamine Dihydrochloride). J. Pharmacol. exp. Ther. 119:163, 1957.

419. Hutcheon, E., et al. Cardiovascular Actions of Hydroxyzine (Atarax). J. Pharmacol. exp. Ther. 118:451-460, 1956.

420. Blackmore, W. P. Effect of Hydroxyzine on Urine Flow in the Dog. Proc. Soc. exp. Biol. (N. Y.) 103:518-520, 1960.

421. Randall, L. O. and T. H. Smith. The Adrenergic Blocking Action of Some Dibenzazepine Derivatives. J. Pharmacol. exp. Ther. 103: 10-23, 1951.

422. Cotton, M., et al. A Comparison of the Effectiveness of Adrenergic Blocking Drugs in Inhibiting the Cardiac Actions of Sympathomimetic Amines. J. Pharmacol. exp. Ther. 121:183-190, 1957.

423. Frommel, E., et al. On the Pharmacology of a New Neuroleptic: The Alpha-isomer of 2-chloro-9 (3-dimethylaminopropylidene)-Thioxanthene or Taractan; Action on Sleep Centers, on Motor Excitation Due to Nikethamide, on Pentetrazol, Electroshock and Psychomotor Excitation Due to Amphetamine. C. R. Soc. Biol. (Paris) 154:1182-1185, 1960.

424. Oberholzer, R. J. H. Experimental Data on Iminodibenzyl Derivative: Tofranil. J. Med. (Porto.) 42:602-605, 1960.

425. Dobkin, A. B. Potentiation of Thiopental Anesthesia by Derivatives and Analogs of Phenothiazine. Anesthesiology 21:292-296, 1960.

426. Gokhale, S., et al. Mechanism of the Initial Adrenergic Effects of Bretylium and Guanethidine. Brit. J. Pharmacol. 20:362-377, 1963.

427. Gyermek, L. and C. Possemato. Potentiation of 5-Hydroxytryptamine by Imipramine. Med. exp. (Basel) 3:225-229, 1960.

428. Benson, W. M., et al. Pharmacologic and Toxicologic Observations on Hydrazine Derivatives of Isonicotinic Acid (Rimifon, Marsilid). Amer. Rev. Tuberc. 65:376-391, 1952.

429. Randall, L. O. and R. E. Bagdon. Pharmacology of Iproniazid and Other Amine Oxidase Inhibitors. Ann. N. Y. Acad. Sci. 80:626-642, 1959.

430. Spector, S., et al. Biochemical and Pharmacological Effects of the Monoamine Oxidase Inhibitors, Iproniazid, 1-Phenyl-2-Hydrazinopropane (JB 516) and 1-Phenyl-3-Hydrazinobutane (JB 835). J. Pharmacol. exp. Ther. 128:15-21, 1960.

431. Bartlet, A. L. The 5-Hydroxytryptamine Content of Mouse Brain and Whole Mice after Treatment with Some Drugs Affecting the Central Nervous System. Brit. J. Pharmacol. 15:140-146, 1960.

432. Wirth, W., et al. On Testing Stimulating Substances (Hydrazine Derivatives) on "Annoyed" Animals. Arch. exp. Path. Pharmakol. 238:62-66, 1960.

433. Green, H. and R. W. Erickson. Effect of Trans-2-Phenylcyclopropylamine upon Norepinephrine Concentration and Monoamine Oxidase Activity of Rat Brain. J. Pharmacol. exp. Ther. 129:237-242, 1960.

434. Spector, S. Effect of Iproniazid on Brain Levels of Norepinephrine and Serotonin. Science 127:704, 1958.

435. Benson, W. M., et al. Comparative Pharmacology of Levorphan, Racemorphan and Dextrorphon and Related Methyl Ethers. J. Pharmacol. exp. Ther. 109:189-200, 1953.

436. Hunter, A. R. The Toxicity of Xylocaine. Brit. J. Anaesth. 23:153-161, 1951.

437. Goldberg, L. Studies on Local Anesthetics. Pharmacological Properties of Homologues and Isomers of Xylocain (Alkyl Amino-Acid Derivatives). Acta physiol. scand. 18:1-18, 1949.

438. Sorel, L. and R. Lejeune. EEG Changes in the Rabbit Following Intravenous Injection of Cocaine. Arch. int. Pharmacodyn. 102:314-334, 1955.

439. Kovalev, I. E. On the Influence of Mezocaine and Zylocaine on the Central Nervous System. Farmikol. i Toksikol. 23:385-390, 1960.

440. Bernard, C. G., et al. On the Evaluation of the Anticonvulsive Effect of Different Local Anesthetics. Arch. int. Pharmacodyn. 108:392-401, 1956.

441. Wagers, P. W. and C. M. Smith. Responses in Dental Nerves of Dogs to Tooth Stimulation and the Effects of Systemically Administered Procaine, Lidocaine and Morphine. J. Pharmacol. exp. Ther. 130:89-105, 1960.

442. Bernhard, C. G., et al. The Difference in Action on Normal and Convulsive Cortical Activity between a Local Anesthetic (Lidocaine) and Barbiturate. Arch. int. Pharmacodyn. 108:408-419, 1956.

443. Gogerty, J. and J. Dille. Pharmacology of d-Lysergic-Acid Morpholide (LSM). J. Pharmacol. exp. Ther. 120:340-348, 1957.

444. Delphant, J. and M. Lanza. Comparative Action of Mescaline, LSD 25, and Yajeine on the Central Temperature of the Rat. J. Physiol. (Paris) 52:70-71, 1960.

445. Weltman, A. S., et al. Endocrine Effects of Lysergic Acid Diethylamide on Male Rats. Fed. Proc. 22:165, 1963.

446. Yui, T. and Y. Takeo. Neuropharmacological Studies on a New Series of Ergot Alkaloids. Jap. J. Pharmacol. 7:157-161, 1958.

447. Key, B. J. and P. B. Bradley. The Effects of Drugs on Conditioning and Habituation to Arousal Stimuli in Animals. Psychopharmacologia 1:450-462, 1960.

448. Passonant, P., et al. The Action of LSD-25 on the Behavior and on the Cortical and Rhinencephalic Rhythms of the Chronic Cat. Electroenceph. clin. Neurophysiol. 8:702, 1956.

449. Apter, J. T. LSD-25 Versus Pentobarbital Sodium. Fed. Proc. 17:5, 1958.

450. Elder, J. T. Phenoxybenzamine (PBA) Antogonism of Lysergic Acid Diethylamide (LSD)-Induced Hyperglycemia. Pharmacologist 5:261, 1963.

451. Dobkin, A. B. and J. H. Havland. Drugs Which Stimulate Affective Behavior. I. Action of Lysergic Acid Diethylamide (LSD-25) Against

Thiopentone Anesthesia in Dogs. Anaesthesia 15:48-54, 1960.

452. Murray, E. J. and S. Chorover. Effects of Lysergic Acid Diethylamine upon Certain Aspects of Memory (Delayed Alternation) in Monkeys. Fed. Proc. 17:381, 1958.

453. Weidmann, H. and A. Cerletti. Investigation of the Pressor Activity of 5-Hydroxytryptamine (Serotonin). Arch. int. Pharmacodyn. 111:98-107, 1957.

454. Meltzer, S. J. and J. Auer. Physiological and Pharmacological Studies of Magnesium Salts. I. General Anesthesia by Subcutaneous Injections. Amer. J. Physiol. 14:366-388, 1905.

455. Gylus, J. A., et al. Pharmacological and Toxicological Properties of 2-Methyl-3-Piperidinopyrazine, a New Antidepressant. Ann. N. Y. Acad. Sci. 107:899-912, 1963.

456. Heise, G. A. and E. Boff. Behavioral Determination of Time and Dose Parameters of Monoamine Oxidase Inhibitors. J. Pharmacol. exp. Ther. 129:155-162, 1960.

457. Berger, F. M., et al. The Pharmacological Properties of 2-Methyl-2-Sec-Butyl-1, 3-Propanediol Dicarbamate (Mebutamate, W-583), a New Centrally Acting Blood Pressure Lowering Agent. J. Pharmacol. exp. Ther. 134: 356-365, 1961.

458. Rowe, G. G., et al. The Effect of Mecamylamine on Coronary Flow, Cardiac Work and Cardiac Efficiency in Normotensive Dogs. J. Lab. clin. Med. 52:883-887, 1958.

459. Lum, B. K. B. and P. L. Rushleigh. Potentiation of Vasoactive Drugs by Ganglionic Blocking Agents. J. Pharmacol. exp. Ther. 132:13-18, 1961.

460. Lakeside Laboratories. Personal Communication.

461. Roszkowski, A. P. A Pharmacological Comparison of Therapeutically Useful Centrally Acting Skeletal Muscle Relaxants. J. Pharmacol. exp. Ther. 129:75-81, 1960.

462. Burke, J. C., et al. The Muscle Relaxant Properties of 2, 2-Dichloro-1-(p-Chlorophenyl)-1, 3-Propanediol-O^3-Carbamate. Arch. int. Pharmacodyn. 134:216-223, 1961.

463. Della Bella, D. and F. Rognoni. Pharmacologic Properties of a New Synthetic Derivative with Central Depressant Activity: 2-2-bis-Chloromethyl-1, 3-Propanediol (Dispranol). Boll. chim. farm. 99:67-78, 1960.

464. Seifter, J., et al. Pharmacology of N-Methyl-ω-Phenyl-Tert-Butylamine. 116th Meeting Am. Chem. Soc. 17L, 1949.

465. Day, M. D. Effect of Sympathomimetic Amines on the Blocking Action of Guanethidine, Bretylium and Xylocholine. Brit. J. Pharmacol. 18:421-439, 1962.

466. Covino, B. G. Antifibrillary Effect of Mephentermine Sulfate (Wyamine) in General Hypothermia. J. Pharmacol. exp. Ther. 122:418-422, 1958.

467. Brofman, B. L., et al. Treatment of Hypotension Accompanying Myocardial Infarction: Use of a Pressor Substance. J. Lab. clin. Med. 36:802, 1950.

468. Fawaz, G. The Effect of Mephentermine on Isolated Dog Hearts, Normal and Pretreated with Reserpine. Brit. J. Pharmacol. 16:309-314, 1961.

469. Aston, R. and H. Cullumbine. The Effects of Combinations of Ataraxics with Hypnotics, LSD and Iproniozid in the Mouse. Arch. int. Pharmacodyn. 126:219-227, 1960.

470. Geller, I. and J. Seifter. The Effects of Meprobamate, Barbiturates, d-Amphetamine and Promazine on Experimentally Induced Conflict in the Rat. Psychopharmacologia (Berl.) 1:482-492, 1960.

471. Takeda, Y. Pharmacological and Toxicological Studies on Tranquilizers. Yakugaku Kenkyu 32:585-616, 1960.

472. Ledebur, I. v., et al. Nalorphine Antagonism of the Narcotic Action of Chlorpromazine, Meprobamate, and Methaminodiazepoxide (Librium). Med. Exptl. 7:177-179, 1962.

473. Hendley, C. D., et al. Effects of Meprobamate (Miltown), Chlorpromazine, and Reserpine on Behavior in the Monkey. Fed. Proc. 15:436, 1956.

474. Barnes, T. C. Effects of Tranquilizers and Antiepileptic Drugs on EEG-Flicker Response and on Convulsive Behavior. Fed. Proc. 17: 347, 1958.

475. Orth, O. S., et al. Subacute Toxicity of

"Thiomerin" Compared to Other Mercurial Diuretics. Fed. Proc. 9:305-306, 1950.

476. Ernst, A. M. Experiments with an O-Methylated Product of Dopamine on Cats. Acta physiol. pharmacol. neerl. 11:48-53, 1962.

477. Parker, J. M. and N. Hildebrand. Mescaline Blocking Effects of Dibenamine. Fed. Proc. 21:419, 1962.

478. Hosko, M. J., Jr. and R. Tislow. Acute Tolerance to Mescaline in the Dog. Fed. Proc. 15:440, 1956.

479. Bridger, W. H. and W. H. Gantt. The Effect of Mescaline on Differentiated Conditional Reflexes. Amer. J. Psychiat. 113:352-360, 1956.

480. Chen, K. K. Pharmacology of Methadone and Related Compounds. Ann. N. Y. Acad. Sci. 51:83-97, 1948.

481. Finnegan, J. K., et al. Observations on the Comparative Pharmacologic Actions of 6-Dimethylamino-4, 4-Diphenyl-3-Heptanone (Amidone) and Morphine. J. Pharmacol. exp. Ther. 92:269-276, 1948.

482. Eddy, N. B. and D. Leimbach. Synthetic Analgesics. II. Dithienylbutenyl and Dithienylbutylamines. J. Pharmacol. exp. Ther. 107: 385-393, 1953.

483. Holten, C. H. and E. Sonne. Action of a Series of Benactyzine-Derivatives and Other Compounds on Stress-Induced Behavior in the Rat. Acta pharmacol. (Kbh.) 11:148-155, 1955.

484. Somers, G. F. Pharmacological Properties of Thalidomide (α-Phtyalimido Glutarmide), a New Sedative Hypnotic Drug. Brit. J. Pharmacol. 15:111-116, 1960.

485. Hauschild, F. The Pharmacology of Phenylalkylamine. Arch. exp. Path. Pharmakol. 195: 647-680, 1940.

486. Owen, J. E., Jr. The Influence of dl, d- and l-Amphetamine and d-Methamphetamine on a Fixed-Ratio Schedule. J. exp. Anal. Behav. 3:293-310, 1960.

487. John, E. R., et al. Differential Effects on Various Conditioned Responses in Cats Caused by Intraventricular and Intramuscular Injections of Reserpine and Other Substances. J. Pharmacol. exp. Ther. 123:193-205, 1958.

488. Hjort, A. M., et al. The Pharmacology of Compounds Related to β-2, 5-Dimethoxy, Phenethyl Amine. J. Pharmacol. exp. Ther. 92:283-290, 1948.

489. De Beer, E. J., et al. The Restoration of Arterial Pressure from Various Hypotensive States by Methoxamine. Arch. int. Pharmacodyn. 104:487-498, 1956.

490. Stormorken, H., et al. Mechanism of Bradycardia by Methoxamine. Arch. int. Pharmacodyn. 120:386-401, 1959.

491. Visscher, F. E., et al. Pharmacology of Pamine Bromide. J. Pharmacol. exp. Ther. 110:188-204, 1954.

492. Smith, S. E. The Pharmacological Actions of 3-4-Dihydroxyphenyl-α-Methylamine (α-Methyldopa), an Inhibitor of 5-Hydroxytryptophan Decarboxylase. Brit. J. Pharmacol. 15: 319-327, 1960.

493. Dangler, H. and G. Reichel. Inhibition of Dopa Decarboxylase by 2-Methyl-3-(3, 4-Dihydroxyphenyl) Alanine (α-methyl Dopa) in vivo. Arch. exp. Path. Pharmakol. 234:275-281, 1958.

494. Westermann, E., et al. Inhibition of Serotonin Formation by α-Methyl-3, 4-Dihydroxyphenyl-L-Alanine. Arch. exp. Path. Pharmakol. 234:194-205, 1958.

495. Sergio, C. and V. G. Longo. Action of Several Drugs on EEG and Behavior of Decorticate Rabbits. Arch. int. Pharmacodyn. 125:65-82, 1960.

496. Maxwell, R. A., et al. Differential Potentiation of Norepinephrine and Epinephrine by Cardiovascular and CNS-Active Agents. J. Pharmacol. exp. Ther. 128:140-144, 1960.

497. Maxwell, R. A., et al. Studies Concerning the Cardiovascular Actions of the Central Nervous Stimulant, Methylphenidate. J. Pharmacol. exp. Ther. 123:22-27, 1958.

498. Maxwell, R. A., et al. A Comparison of Some of the Cardiovascular Actions of Methylphenidate and Cocaine. J. Pharmacol. exp. Ther. 126:250-257, 1959.

499. Eddy, N. B. Pharmacology of Metopon and Other New Analgesic Opium Derivatives. Ann. N. Y. Acad. Sci. 51:51-58, 1948.

500. Chesler, A., et al. A Study of the Comparative Toxic Effects of Morphine on the Fetal,

Newborn and Adult Rat. J. Pharmacol. exp. Ther. 75:363-366, 1942.

501. Haag, H. B., et al. Pharmacologic Observations on 1, 1-Diphenyl-1-(dimethylaminoisopropyl)-butanone-2. Fed. Proc. 6:334, 1947.

502. Hatcher, R. A. and C. Eggleston. Studies on the Absorption of Drugs. J. Amer. med. Ass. 63:(1):469-473, 1914.

503. Himmelsbach, C. K., et al. A Method for Testing Addiction, Tolerance and Abstinence in the Rat. J. Pharmacol. exp. Ther. 53:179-188, 1935.

504. Blozovski, M. and J. Jacob. The Effect of Morphine on the Behavior of Mice Trained to Run through an Elevated Maze. Arch. int. Pharmacodyn. 124:422-435, 1960.

505. Olds, H., and R. P. Travis. Effects of Chlorpromazine, Meprobamate, Pentobarbital and Morphine on Self-Stimulation. J. Pharmacol. exp. Ther. 128:397-404, 1960.

506. Tedeschi, D. H., et al. Analgesic and Other Neuropharmacologic Effects of Phenazocine (NIH 7519, Prinadol) Compared with Morphine. J. Pharmacol. exp. Ther. 130:431-435, 1960.

507. Zirm, K. L. and A. Pongratz. The Analgetic Action of the Pyridin-3-Carbonic Acid Bis Ester of Morphine. Arzneimittel-Forsch. 10: 137-139, 1960.

508. Wright, C. I. and F. A. Barbour. The Respiratory Effects of Morphine, Codeine and Related Substances. J. Pharmacol. exp. Ther. 53:34-45, 1935.

509. Longo, V. G. Electroencephalographic Atlas for Pharmacological Research. Elsevier Publ. Co., New York and Amsterdam, 1962.

510. Takagi, H., et al. The Effect of Analgesics on the Spinal Reflex Activity of the Cat. Jap. J. Pharmacol. 4:176-187, 1955.

511. Fühner, H. Pharmacological Actions of Muscarine Derivatives. Arch. exp. Path. Pharm. 61:283-296, 1909.

512. Mattila, M. and P. Lavikainen. The Mouse Tail Reaction Induced by Morphine and the Sedative Action after Reserpine and Nalorphine. Ann. Med. exp. Fenn. 38:115-120, 1960.

513. Hart, E. R. and E. L. McCawley. The Pharmacology of N-Allylnormorphine as Compared with Morphine. J. Pharmacol. exp. Ther. 182:339-348, 1944.

514. Kirvoy, W. A. and R. A. Huggins. The Action of Morphine, Methadone, Meperidine and Nalorphine on Dorsal Root Potentials of Cat Spinal Cord. J. Pharmacol. exp. Ther. 134:210-213, 1961.

515. Unna, K. Antagonistic Effect of N-Allyl-Normorphine upon Morphine. J. Pharmacol. exp. Ther. 79:27-31, 1943.

516. Goldstein, L. and J. Aldunate. Quantitative Electroencephalographic Studies of the Effects of Morphine and Nalorphine on Rabbit Brain. J. Pharmacol. exp. Ther. 130:204-211, 1960.

517. Brown, B. B., et al. A Comparative Study of Tetramethoquin, a New Parasympathetic Stimulant, Neostigmine and Physostigmine. Arch. int. Pharmacodyn. 81:276-289, 1950.

518. Haley, T. J. and B. M. Rhodes. A Note on the Acute Toxicity of Neostigmine Methyl Bromide in the Rat. J. Am. pharm. Ass. 39: 701, 1950.

519. Aeschlimann, J. A. and M. Reinert. The Pharmacological Action of Some Analogues of Physostigmine. J. Pharmacol. exp. Ther. 43:413-444, 1931.

520. Heathcote, R. St. A. The Pharmacological Action of Eseridine. J. Pharmacol. exp. Ther. 46:375-385, 1932.

521. Polonovski, M. and M. Polonovski. Alkaloidal Derivatives with Attenuated Toxicity. C. R. Acad. Sci. (Paris) 181:887-888, 1925.

522. Carlsson, A. and N. Hillarp. Formation of Phenolic Acids in Brain After Administration of 3, 4-Dihydroxyphenylalanine. Acta physiol. scand. 55:95-100, 1962.

523. P'an, S. Y., et al. Anticonvulsant Effect of Nialamide and Diphenylhydantoin. Proc. Soc. 108:680-683, 1961.

524. Larson, P. S., et al. Studies on the Fate of Nicotine in the Body. VI. Observations on the Relative Rate of Elimination of Nicotine by the Dog, Cat, Rabbit and Mouse. J. Pharmacol. exp. Ther. 95:506-508, 1949.

525. Heubner, W. and J. Papierkowski. On the Toxicity of Nicotine in Mice. Arch. exp. Path. Pharmakol. 188:605-610, 1938.

526. Behrend, A. and C. H. Thienes. The Development of Tolerance to Nicotine by Rats. J. Pharmacol. exp. Ther. 48:317-325, 1933.

527. Chen, K. K., et al. Toxicity of Nicotinic Acid. Proc. Soc. exp. Biol. (N. Y.) 38:241-245, 1938.

528. Hatcher, R. A. Nicotine Tolerance in Rabbits and the Difference in the Total Dose in Adult and Young Guinea Pigs. Amer. J. Physiol. 11:17-27, 1904.

529. Bonta, I. L., et al. A Newly Developed Motility Apparatus and its Applicability in Two Pharmacological Designs. Arch. int. Pharmacodyn. 129:381-394, 1960.

530. Hardt, A. and R. Hotovy. Methods of Testing for Compounds with Curare-Like Action. Arch. exp. Path. Pharmakol. 209:264-278, 1950.

531. Smith, C. S., et al. Study of the Effect of Nicotinism in the Albino Rat. J. Pharmacol. exp. Ther. 55:274-287, 1935.

532. Kuschinsky, G. and R. Hotovy. On the Central Stimulative Action of Nicotine. Klin. Wschr. 22:649-650, 1943.

533. Knapp, D. E. and E. F. Comino. Evidence for a Nicotinic Receptor in the Central Nervous System Related to EEG Arousal. Fed. Proc. 20:307, 1961.

534. Novikova, A. A. Influence of Nicotine upon Reflex Activity. Bull. eksp. Biol. Med. S.S.S.R. 9:38-42, 1940.

535. Schaepdryver, A. F. de. Hypertensive Responses in Reserpinized Dogs. Arch. int. Pharmacodyn. 124:45-52, 1960.

536. Behrens, B. and E. Reichelt. A Comparison of Cardiazol and Coramin in an Animal Experiment. Klin. Wschr. 12:1860-1862, 1933.

537. Hildebrandt, F. Pentamethylentetrazol (Cardiazol). Heffter's Hdb. E. 5:151-183, 1937.

538. Albus, G. Animal Experiments with Commercial Stimulants with Particular Consideration of Cardiazole and Coramine. Arch. int. Path. Pharmakol. 182:471-476, 1936.

539. Eichholtz, F. and T. Kirsch. The Effect of Depressor Substances on Cocaine Convulsions. Arch. exp. Path. Pharmakol. 184:674-679, 1937.

540. Heubner, W. and A. v. Nyary. Cumulation of the Digitalis Glucosides. Arch. exp. Path. Pharmakol. 177:60-73, 1934.

541. White, A. C. The Pharmacological and Toxic Action of Digoxin. J. Pharmacol. exp. Ther. 52:1-22, 1934.

542. Boyajy, L. D. and C. B. Nash. Influence of Reserpine on Fibrillatory and Positive Inotropic Responses to Ouabain. Fed. Proc. 22: 185, 1963.

543. Henderson, F. G., et al. Pharmacologic Studies of 6, 7-Dimethoxy, 1-(4'-ethoxy-3'-methoxybenzyl)3-Methyl-Isoquinoline. J. Amer. pharm. Ass. 40:207, 1951.

544. Macht, D. I. A Pharmacologic and Clinical Study of Papaverin. Arch. intern. Med. 17: 786-805, 1916.

545. Leopold-Lowenthal, H. On the Pharmacological Properties of 1-Methyl-butyl-2-Phenyl-2-Hydroxypropionate (Spasmol). Wien med. Wschr. 101:61, 1951.

546. Drommond, F. G., et al. Toxicity of Some Opium Alkaloids. Acta pharmacol. (Kbh.) 6: 235-249, 1950.

547. Tunger, H. The Duration of Narcosis and the Narcotic Range of Nonspecific Narcotics in Different Methods of Administration. Arch. exp. Path. Pharmakol. 160:74-91, 1931.

548. Figot, P. P., et al. The Estimation and Significance of Paraldehyde Levels in Blood and Brain. Acta pharmacol. (Kbh.) 8:290-304, 1952.

549. Kay, F. A., et al. Studies on Paraldehyde. I. The Median Lethal Dose, LD_{50}, of Paraldehyde for Guinea Pigs. Anesthesiology 5: 182-185, 1944.

550. Jenney, E. H. and C. C. Pfeiffer. The Convulsant Effect of Hydrazides and the Antidotal Effect of Anticonvulsants and Metabolites. J. Pharmacol. exp. Ther. 122:110-123, 1958.

551. Everett, G. M. Pharmacologic Studies of Some Nonhydrazine MAO Inhibitors. Ann. N. Y. Acad. Sci. 107:1068-1077, 1963.

552. Spector, S. Monoamine Oxidase in Control of Brain Serotonin and Norepinephrine Content. Ann. N. Y. Acad. Sci. 107:856-861, 1963.

553. Schoepke, H. G. and R. G. Wiegand. Relation between Norepinephrine Accumulation or Depletion and Blood Pressure Responses in the Cat and Rat Following Pargyline Administration. Ann. N. Y. Acad. Sci. 107:924-934, 1963.

554. Taylor, J. D., et al. A New Non-Hydrazide Monoamine Oxidase Inhibitor (A 19120) (N-Methyl-N-Benzyl-2-Propynylamine Hydrochloride). Fed. Proc. 19:278, 1960.

555. Calesnick, B. et .al. Combined Action of Cardiotoxic Drugs: A Study on the Acute Toxicity of Combined Quinidine, Meperidine, Pentobarbital, Procaine, and Procaine Amide. J. Pharmacol. exp. Ther. 102:138-143, 1951.

556. Carmichael, E. B. and L. C. Posey. Toxicity of Nembutal for Guinea Pigs. Proc. Soc. exp. Biol. (N. Y.) 33:527-528, 1936.

557. Westhues, M. and R. Fritsch. The Narcosis of Animals. Paul Parcy, Berlin, 1961.

558. Krop, S. and H. Gold. Comparative Study of Several Barbiturates with Observations on Irreversible Neurological Disturbances. J. Pharmacol. exp. Ther. 88:260-267, 1946.

559. White, R. P. and L. D. Boyajy. Comparison of Physostigmine and Amphetamine in Antagonizing the Electroencephalogram (EEG) Effects of Central Nervous System Depressants. Proc. Soc. exp. Biol. (N. Y.) 102:479-483, 1959.

560. Schallek, W., et al. Central Depressant Effects of Methyprylon. J. Pharmacol. exp. Ther. 118:139-147, 1956.

561. Kneip, P. Climbing Impulse and Climbing Test. Arch. int. Pharmacodyn. 126:238-245, 1960.

562. Tsobkallo, G. I. and M. K. Kalinina. Effect of Barbamyl, Nembutal and Thiopental on the Higher Nervous Activity of Rabbits. Pavlov J. High. Nerv. Act. 10:644-652, 1960.

563. Bradley, P. B. and B. J. Key. The Effect of Drugs on Arousal Responses Produced by Electrical Stimulation of the Reticular Formation. Electroenceph. clin. Neurophysiol. 10: 97-110, 1958.

564. Pfeiffer, C. C., et al. Comparative Study of the Effect of Meprobamate on the Conditioned Response, on Strychnine and Pentenetetrazol Thresholds, on the Normal Electroencephalogram, and on Polysynaptic Reflexes. Ann. N. Y. Acad. Sci. 67:734-743, 1957.

565. Martin, W. R. and C. G. Eades. A Comparative Study of the Effect of Drugs on Activation and Vasomotor Responses Evoked by Midbrain Stimulation: Atropine, Pentobarbital, Chlorpromazine and Chlorpromazine Sulfoxide. Psychopharmacologia 1:303-335, 1960.

566. Abdulian, D. H., et al. Effects of Central Nervous System Depressants on Inhibition And Facilitation of the Patellar Reflex. Arch. int. Pharmacodyn. 128:169-186, 1960.

567. Mitchell, J. C. and F. A. King. The Effects of Chlorpromazine on Water Maze Learning Retention, and Stereotyped Behavior in the Rat. Psychopharmacologia 1:463-468, 1960.

568. Domer, F. R. and W. Feldberg. The Effect of Administration of Drugs into the Cerebral Ventricles. Brit. J. Pharmacol. 15:578-587, 1960.

569. McOmie, W. A. Local and Systemic Effects of 2-Methyl 2,4-Pentanedial (Hexylene Glycol). Fed. Proc. 6:357, 1947.

570. Hildebrandt, F. Pyridin-β-Carboxylic Acid Diethylamide (Coramin). Heffter's Hdb. E. 5: 128-150.

571. Gross, E. G. and R. M. Featherstone. Studies with Tetrazole Derivatives. I. Some Pharmacologic Properties of Aliphatic Substitutes Pentamethylene Tetrazole Derivatives. J. Pharmacol. exp. Ther. 87:291-305, 1946.

572. Werner, H. W. and A. L. Tatum. A Comparative Study of the Stimulant Analeptics Picrotoxin, Metrazol and Coramine. J. Pharmacol. exp. Ther. 66:260-278, 1939.

573. Ziph, K., et al. The Antagonistic Action of Cardiazole, Coramine, Hexetone, Strychnine and Icoral to Narcotics. Arch. exp. Path. Pharmakol. 185:113-124, 1937.

574. Hildebrandt, F. and J. Voss. Absorption of Cardiazol Following Oral Administration. München med. Wchnschr. 73:862, 1926.

575. Chusid, J. and L. Kopeloff. Chlordiazepoxide as an Anticonvulsant in Monkeys. Proc. Soc. exp. Biol. (N. Y.) 109:546-548, 1962.

576. Wallace, G. D., et al. Restraint of Chimpanzees with Perphenazine. J. Am. vet. med. Ass. 136:222-224, 1960.

577. High, J. P., et al. Pharmacology of Fluphenazine (Prolixin). Toxicol. appl. Pharmacol. 2: 540-552, 1960.

578. Taeschler, M., et al. On the Significance of Various Pharmacodynamic Properties of Phenothiazine Derivatives for their Clinical Effectiveness. Psychiat. et Neurol. (Basel) 139:85-104, 1960.

579. Scott, C. C., et al. Comparison of the Pharmacologic Properties of Some New Analgesic Substances. Curr. Res. Anesth. 26:12-17, 1947.

580. Gruber, C. M. and E. R. Hart. The Pharmacology and Toxicology of the Ethyl Ester of 1-Methyl-4-Phenyl-Piperidine-4-Carboxylic Acid (Demerol). J. Pharmacol. exp. Ther. 73:319-334, 1941.

581. Foster, R. H. K. and A. L. Carman. Studies in Analgesia: Piperidine Derivatives with Morphine-Like Activity. J. Pharmacol. exp. Ther. 91:195-209, 1947.

582. Emele, J. F., et al. The Analgesic Activity of Phenelzine and Other Compounds. J. Pharmacol. exp. Ther. 134:206-209, 1961.

583. Ben, M., et al. Cardiovascular Activity of β-Phenylethylhydrazine (Phenelzine). Angiology 11:62-66, 1960.

584. Eltherington, L. G. and A. Horita. Some Pharmacological Actions of Beta-Phenylisopropylhydrazine (PIH). J. Pharmacol. exp. Ther. 128:7-14, 1960.

585. Buchel, L. and J. Levy. Contribution to the Study of the Effects of Hydrazine-2-Phenyl-3-Propane (PIH) on the Central Nervous System, Compared with Those of 1-Isonicotinyl-2-Isopropylhydrazine (Iproniazid). I. Influence on Experimental Hypnosis. Anesth. et Analg. 17:289-312, 1960.

586. Buckley, J. P., et al. The Pharmacology of Beta-Phenylisopropylhydrazine. Fed. Proc. 19:278, 1960.

587. Schaffarsick, R. W. and B. J. Brown. The Anticonvulsant Activity and Toxicity of Methylparafynol (Dormison) and Some Other Alcohols. Science 116:663-665, 1952.

588. Fitch, R. H. and A. L. Tatum. The Duration of Action of the Barbituric Acid Hypnotics as a Basis of Classification. J. Pharmacol. exp. Ther. 44:325-335, 1932.

589. Anderson, E. G. and D. D. Bonnycastle. A Study of the Central Depressant Action of Pentobarbital, Phenobarbital and Diethyl Ether in Relationship to Increases in Brain 5-Hydroxytryptamine. J. Pharmacol. exp. Ther. 130:138-143, 1960.

590. Wilson, H. and J. P. Long. The Effect of Hemicholinium (HC-3) at Various Peripheral Cholinergic Transmitting Sites. Arch. int. Pharmacodyn. 120:343-352, 1959.

591. Bodo, R. C. de and K. F. Prescott. The Antidiuretic Action of Barbiturates (Phenobarbital, Amytal, Pentobarbital) and the Mechanism Involved in this Action. J. Pharmacol. exp. Ther. 85:222-233, 1945.

592. Truitt, E. B., Jr., et al. Measurement of Brain Excitability by Use of Hexafluorodiethyl Ether (Indoklon). J. Pharmacol. exp. Ther. 129:445-453, 1960.

593. De Salva, S. Continuous Intravenous Infusion of Strychnine in Rats: III. Endocrine Influences. Arch. int. Pharmacodyn. 125:355-361, 1960.

594. Weaver, L. C., et al. Central Nervous System Effects of a Local Anesthetic, Dyclonine. Toxicol. appl. Pharmacol. 2:616-627, 1960.

595. Delgado, J. M. R., et al. Effect of Amphenidone on the Brain of the Conscious Monkey. Arch. int. Pharmacodyn. 125:161-171, 1960.

596. Vogel, G. and L. Ther. The Behavior of the Cotton Rat as Determinant of Neuroleptic Ratio of Central-Depressing Compounds. Arzneimittel-Forsch. 10:806-808, 1960.

597. Domino, E. F., et al. Differential Effects of Some CNS Depressants on a Quantitative Shock Avoidance Response in the Dog. J. Pharmacol. exp. Ther. 122:20A, 1958.

598. Scheer, E. The Depressant Effect of Sodium Ethylcrotyl Barbiturate on the Central Nervous System and Influences on Blood Pressure and Blood Sugar. Acta Biol. et Med. Ger. 5:545-560, 1960.

599. Sobek, V. Effects of Barbiturates on Reflex Peristaltic Inhibition. Farmakol. i Toksikol. 23:17-20, 1960.

600. Schapiro, S. Effect of a Catechol Amine Blocking Agent (Dibenzyline) on Organ Content and Urine Excretion of Noradrenaline and Adrenaline. Acta physiol. scand. 42:371-375, 1958.

601. Quinn, G. P., et al. Biochemical and Pharmacological Studies of RO1-9569 (Tetrabena-

zine), a Non-Indole Tranquilizing Agent with Reserpine-Like Effects. J. Pharmacol. exp. Ther. 127:103-109, 1959.

602. Innes, I. R. Identification of the Smooth Muscle Excitatory Receptors for Ergot Alkaloids. Brit. J. Pharmacol. 19:120-128, 1962.

603. Meier, R., et al. A New Imidazoline Derivative with Marked Adrenolytic Properties. Proc. Soc. exp. Biol. (N. Y.) 71:70-72, 1949.

604. Furchgott, R. F. In: Ciba Foundation Symposium, eds. Vane, J. R., et al. Little Brown, Boston, 1960, p. 246.

605. Hazleton, L. W., et al. Toxicity of Phenylbutazone (Butazolidin). Fed. Proc. 12:330, 1953.

606. Kuschinsky, G. and K. Oberdisse. Circulatory Effects of Meta-Sympatole. Arch. exp. Path. Pharm. 162:46-55, 1931.

607. Warren, M. R. and H. W. Werner. The Central Stimulant Action of Some Vasopressor Amines. J. Pharmacol. exp. Ther. 85: 119-121, 1945.

608. Chessin, M., et al. Biochemical and Pharmacological Studies of β-Phenylhydrazine and Selected Related Compounds. Ann. N. Y. Acad. Sci. 80:597-608, 1959.

609. Way, E. L. Barbiturate Antagonism of Isonipecaine Convulsions and Isonipecaine Potentiation of Barbiturate Depression. J. Pharmacol. exp. Ther. 87:265-272, 1946.

610. Gruhzit, O. M. Sodium Diphenyl Hydantoinate: Pharmacologic and Histopathologic Studies. Arch. Path. 28:761-762, 1939.

611. Knoefel, P. K. and G. Lehmann. The Anticonvulsive Action of Diphenyl Hydantoin and Some Related Compounds. J. Pharmacol. exp. Ther. 72:194-201, 1942.

612. Everett, G. M. and R. K. Richards. Comparative Anti-Convulsive Action of 3, 5, 5-Trimethyloxazolidine-2, 4-Dione (Tridione), Dilantin and Phenobarbital. J. Pharmacol. exp. Ther. 81:402-407, 1944.

613. Esplin, D. W. and J. W. Freston. Physiological and Pharmacological Analysis of Spinal Cord Convulsions. J. Pharmacol. exp. Ther. 130:68-80, 1960.

614. Heubner, W. Pharmacological and Chemical Investigation of Physostigmine. Arch. exp. Path. Pharmakol. 53:313-330, 1905.

615. Zetler, G., et al. Research Toward a Pharmacological Differentiation of Cataleptic Effects. Arch. exp. Path. Pharmakol. 238:468-501, 1960.

616. Hjort, A. M. and E. J. deBeer. The Effect of the Diet upon the Anesthetic Qualities of Some Hypnotics. J. Pharmacol. exp. Ther. 65:79-88, 1939.

617. Swanson, E. E. and K. K. Chen. The Pharmacological Action of Coriamyrtin. J. Pharmacol. exp. Ther. 57:410-418, 1936.

618. Apter, J. T. Analeptic Action of Lysergic Acid Diethylamide (LSD-25) Against Pentobarbital. Arch. Neurol. Psychiat. (Chic.) 79: 711-715, 1958.

619. Holck, H. G. O. and P. R. Cannon. On the Cause of the Delayed Death in the Rat by Isopropyl Betabromallyl Barbituric Acid (Nostal) and Some Related Barbiturates. J. Pharmacol. exp. Ther. 57:289-309, 1936.

620. Zablocka, B. and D. W. Esplin. Central Excitatory and Depressant Effects of Pilocarpine in Rats and Mice. J. Pharmacol. exp. Ther. 140:162-169, 1963.

621. Singh, S. D. and H. J. Eysenck. Conditioned Emotional Response in the Rat. III. Drug Antagonism. J. Gen. Psychol. 63:275-285, 1960.

622. Stone, G. C. Effects of Some Centrally Acting Drugs upon Learning of Escape and Avoidance Habits. J. comp. physiol. Psychol. 53:33-37, 1960.

623. Larson, R. E. and G. L. Plaa. Effect of Spinal Cord Transection on CCl_4 Hepatotoxicity. Fed. Proc. 22:189, 1963.

624. Gettler, A. O. and J. Baine. The Toxicology of Cyanide. Amer. J. med. Sci. 195:182-188, 1938.

625. Lindgren, P. and A. Sundwall. Parasympatholytic Effects of TMB-4 (1, 1-Trimethylene-bis (4-Formylpyridinium Bromide)-Dioxime) and Some Related Oximes in the Cat. Acta pharmacol. (Kbh.) 17:69-83, 1960.

626. Santi, R., et al. Pharmacological Action of N, N-Diisopropylammonium Dichloroacetate (DIEDI). Minerva Med. 51, Suppl. 71:2909-2919, 1960.

627. McKinney, S. E., et al. Benemid, p-(Di-n-Propylsulamyl)-Benzoic Acid: Toxicologic Properties. J. Pharmacol. exp. Ther. 102: 208-214, 1951.

628. Seiffer, J. et al. The Toxicity of N, N'-Dibenzylethylenediamine (DBED) and DBED Dipenecillin. Antibiot. et Chemother. (Basel) 1: 504-508, 1951.

629. Naranjo, P. and E. B. de Naranjo. Local Anesthetic Activity of Some Antihistamines and its Relationship with the Antihistaminic and Anticholinergic Activities. Arch. int. Pharmacodyn. 113:313-335, 1958.

630. Richards, R. K. and K. E. Kueter. Competitive Inhibition of Procaine Convulsions in Guinea Pigs. J. Pharmacol. exp. Ther. 87:42-52, 1946.

631. Schneider, J. A. and F. F. Yonkman. Species Differences in the Respiratory and Cardiovascular Response to Serotonin (5-Hydroxytryptamine). J. Pharmacol. exp. Ther. 111:84-98, 1954.

632. Ilyuchenok, R. Y. Comparative Study of the Influence of Chlorpromazine and Propazine on the Bioelectric Activity of the Cerebrum. Zh. Nevopat. Psikhiat. 60:202-209, 1960.

633. Ekstrom, N. and F. Sandberg. A Method for Quantitative Determination of the Inhibitory Action on C.A.R. of Mice. Arzneimittel-Forsch. 12:1208-1209, 1962.

634. Schneider, J. A. Further Characterization of Central Effects of Reserpine (Serpasil). Am. J. Physiol. 181:64-68, 1955.

635. Innes, I. R. Sensitization of the Heart and Nictitating Membrane of the Cat to Sympathomimetic Amines by Antihistamine Drugs. Brit. J. Pharmacol. 13:6-10, 1958.

636. Black, J. W. and J. S. Stephenson. Pharmacology of a New Adrenergic Beta-Receptor Blocking Compound (Nethalide). Lancet 2: 311-314, 18 Aug., 1962.

637. Goldberg, M. E. and G. V. Rossi. The Effect of Anticholinergic Compounds on Several Components of Gastric Secretion in Pylorus-Ligated Rats. J. Amer. pharm. Ass. 49:543-547, 1960.

638. Abbott, C. E. B., et al. Effect of Propantheline Bromide (Pro-Banthine) on Fluid and Electrolyte Loss in Dogs with Pyloric Obstruction. Canad. med. Ass. J. 76:176-180, 1957.

639. Krayer, O., et al. Studies on Veratrum Alkaloids. VI. Protoveratrine: Its Comparative Toxicity and its Circulatory Action. J. Pharmacol. exp. Ther. 82:167-186, 1944.

640. Swiss, E. D. and R. O. Bauer. Acute Toxicity of Veratrum Derivatives. Proc. Soc. exp. Biol. (N.Y.) 76:847-849, 1951.

641. Haas, H. T. A. Pharmacology of Germerine and its Degradation Products. I. Arch. exp. Path. Pharmakol. 189:397-410, 1938.

642. Martini, L. and L. Calliauw. On the Pharmacology of Protoveratrine in Dogs. Arch. int. Pharmacodyn. 101:49-67, 1955.

643. Mosey, L. and A. Kaplan. Respiratory Effects of Potent Hypotensive Derivatives of Veratrum. J. Pharmacol. exp. Ther. 104: 67-75, 1952.

644. Woolley, D. W. and N. K. Campbell. Serotonin-Like and Antiserotonin Properties of Psilocybin and Psilocin. Science 136:777-778, 1962.

645. Maxwell, G. M., et al. The Effect of Psilocybin upon the Systemic, Pulmonary and Coronary Circulation of the Intact Dog. Arch. int. Pharmacodyn. 137:108-115, 1962.

646. Castillo, J. C., et al. A Pharmacological Study of N-Methyl-N'-(4-Chlorobenzhydryl) Piperazine Dihydrochloride—a New Antihistamine. J. Pharmacol. exp. Ther. 96: 388-395, 1949.

647. Halpern, B. N. and M. Briot. Comparison of the Acute Toxicity of Several Synthetic Antihistaminics in the Rat. C. R. Soc. Biol. (Paris) 144:887-890, 1950.

648. Swift, J. G. A Study of Sustained Ionic Release Antihistamine. Arch. int. Pharmacodyn. 124:341-348, 1960.

649. Virno, M., et al. Action of Histamine on the Jugular Venous Pressure and Cerebral Circulation of the Dog. Effects of Antihistaminic Drugs (Pyrilamine and Chlorpheniramine) and a Histamine Liberating Agent (48/80 B.W.). J. Pharmacol. exp. Ther. 118: 63-76, 1956.

650. Binet, D. The Study of Polyuria in Convalescence from Acute Sickness. Rev. med. Suisse rom. 15:329-341, 1885.

651. Gibbs, W. and H. A. Hare. Systematic Investigation of Related Chemicals on Animal Organisms. Arch. f. Physiol. (Leipz.) 1:344-359, 1890.

652. Gatgounis, J. and R. P. Walton. Resorcinol Isomers and Pentylenetetrazol; their Centrally Mediated Sympathetic Circulatory Effects. J. Pharmacol. exp. Ther. 127:363-371, 1959.

653. Yoshi, N., et al. Studies on the Unit Discharge of Brainstem Reticular Formation in the Cat. II. Effect of Catechol, Amphetamine, Nembutal and Megimide. Med. J. Osaka Univ. 11:19-33, 1960.

654. Neisser, A. Clinical and Experimental Findings on the Action of Pyrogallus Acid. Z. klin. Med. 1:88-108, 1880.

655. Wylie, D. W. Augmentation of the Pressor Response to Guanethedine by Inhibition of Catechol-O-Methyltransferase. Nature 189: 490-491, 1961.

656. Udenfriend, S., et al. Inhibitors of Norepinephrine Metabolism in vivo. Arch. Biochem. 84:249-251, 1959.

657. Bonsmann, M. R. The Pharmacology of the Quinine Alkaloids. Arch. exp. Path. Pharmakol. 205:129-136, 1948.

658. Kirchmann, L. L. Detoxification of Quinidine by Synephrine. Arch. exp. Path. Pharmakol. 192:639-644, 1939.

659. Scott, C. C., et al. Comparison of the Pharmacologic Action of Quinidine and Dihydroquinidine. J. Pharmacol. exp. Ther. 84: 184-188, 1945.

660. Cole, J. and D. Dearnaley. Contrasting Tail and other Responses to Morphine and Reserpine in Rats and Mice. Experientia (Basel) 16:78-80, 1960.

661. Brodie, B. B. and P. A. Shore. A Concept for a Role of Serotonin and Norepinephrine as Chemical Mediators in the Brain. Ann. N. Y. Acad. Sci. 66:631-642, 1957.

662. Burn, J. H. and D. B. McDougal, Jr. The Effect of Reserpine on Gangrene Produced by Thiopental in the Mouse Tail. J. Pharmacol. exp. Ther. 131:167-170, 1961.

663. Paasonen, M. K. and O. Krayer. Effect of Reserpine upon the Mammalian Heart. Fed. Proc. 16:326-327, 1957.

664. Canal, N. and A. Maffei-Faccioli. Reversal of the Reserpine-Induced Depletion of Brain Serotonin by a Monoamine Oxidase Inhibitor. J. Neurochem. 5:99-100, 1959.

665. Muscholl, E., and M. Vogt. The Action of Reserpine on the Peripheral Sympathetic System. J. Physiol. (Lond.) 141:132-155, 1958.

666. Sheppard, H. and J. H. Zimmerman. Reserpine and the Levels of Serotonin and Norepinephrine in the Brain. Nature 185:40-41, 1960.

667. Shore, P. A., et al. Release of Brain Norepinephrine by Reserpine. Fed. Proc. 16: 335-336, 1957.

668. Wilson, C. W. M., et al. The Effects of Reserpine on Uptake of Epinephrine in Brain and Certain Areas Outside the Blood-Brain Barrier. J. Pharmacol. exp. Ther. 135:11-16, 1961.

669. Trendelenburg, U. and J. S. Gravenstein. Effect of Reserpine Pretreatment on Stimulation of the Accelerans Nerve of the Dog. Science 128:901-902, 1958.

670. Brady, J. V. Animal Experimental Evaluation of Drug Effects upon Behavior. Fed. Proc. 17:1031-1043, 1958.

671. Weiskrantz, L. and W. A. Wilson, Jr. The Effects of Reserpine on Emotional Behavior of Normal and Brain-Operated Monkeys. Ann. N. Y. Acad. Sci. 61:36-55, 1955.

672. Tui, C. and C. Debruille. The Comparative Toxicity and Effectiveness of Scopolamine Hydrobromide ($C_{17}H_{21}O_4N \cdot HBr$) and Scopolamine Aminoxide Hydrobromide ($C_{17}H_{21}O_5N \cdot HBr$). Am. J. Pharm. 117:319-326, 1945.

673. Frommel, E., et al. On the Pharmacodynamic Action of a New Tranquilizer: Methaminodiazepoxide, or Librium. An Experimental Study. Thérapie 15:1233-1244, 1960.

674. Gruhzit, O. M. and A. W. Dox. A Pharmacologic Study of Certain Thiobarbiturates. J. Pharmacol. exp. Ther. 60:125-142, 1937.

675. Silvestrini, B., et al. Action of Synchronizing and Desynchronizing Drugs on Strychnine Induced Convulsive Cortical Activity. Fed. Proc. 16:336, 1957.

676. Costa, E. and G. Zetler. Interactions between Epinephrine and Psychotomimetic Drugs on Cat Nictitating Membrane. Fed. Proc. 17: 360, 1958.

677. Winter, D. and M. Timar. Experimental Studies on the Rehypnosis of Animals Just Awakened from Barbiturate Anesthesia. Pharmazie 17:454-455, 1962.

678. Revzin, A. M. and E. Costa. Effects of Exogenous Serotonin on Paleocortical Excitability. Am. J. Physiol. 198:959-961, 1960.

679. Zilberstein, R. Effects of Reserpine, Serotonin and Vasopressin on the Survival of Cold-Stressed Rats. Nature 185:249, 1960.

680. Soulairac, A. and M. L. Soulairac. Action of Reserpine, Serotonin and Iproniazid on the Feeding Behavior of the Rat. C. R. Soc. Biol. (Paris) 154:510-513, 1960.

681. Laroche, M. J. and B. B. Brodie. Lack of Relationship between Inhibition of Monoamine Oxidase and Potentiation of Hexobarbital Hypnosis. J. Pharmacol. exp. Ther. 130:134-137, 1960.

682. Smith, P. K. and W. E. Hambourger. Antipyretic and Toxic Effects of Combinations of Acetanilid with Sodium Bromide and with Caffein. J. Pharmacol. exp. Ther. 55:200-205, 1935.

683. Roholm, K. Fluorine and Fluorine Compounds. Heffter's Hdb. E. 7:1-62, 1938.

684. Muehlberger, C. W. Toxicity Studies of Fluorine Insecticides. J. Pharmacol. exp. Ther. 39:246-248, 1930.

685. Lehman, A. J. Chemicals in Food: A Report to the Association of Food and Drug Officials on Current Developments. Assoc. Food & Drug Officials U.S. Quart. Bull. 15: 122-133, 1951.

686. Ambard, L. and M. S. Trautmann. Demonstration of the Existence of Different Invertases. C. R. Soc. Biol. (Paris) 125:133-135, 1937.

687. Leake, C. D. The Toxicity of Sodium Fluoride in Intravenous Injection in Rabbits. J. Pharmacol. exp. Ther. 33:279-280, 1928.

688. Becker, T., et al. A Theory of Chlorate Poisoning. Arch. exp. Path. Pharmakol. 201: 197-209, 1943.

689. Oltman, T. V. and L. A. Crandal, Jr. The Acute Toxicity of Glyceryl Trinitrate and Sodium Nitrite in Rabbits. J. Pharmacol. exp. Ther. 41:121-126, 1931.

690. Hesse, E. Detoxification of Nitrites. Arch. exp. Path. Pharmakol. 126:209-221, 1927.

691. Dossin, F. Contribution to the Experimental Study of Hypotensive Medication. Arch. int. Pharmacodyn. 21:425-465, 1911.

692. Zipf, H. F. and G. Triller. α-Isoparteine and α-Didehydrosparteine. Arch. exp. Path. Pharmakol. 200:536-550, 1943.

693. Lu, G. Sparteine on Mammalian Circulations. Arch. int. Pharmacodyn. 89:209-222, 1963.

694. Lu, G. Dual Vasomotor Actions of Sparteine. Arch. int. Pharmacodyn. 89:129-144, 1952.

695. Amann, A., et al. A Comparative Study of Strychnine and Strychnine Derivatives. Arch. exp. Path. Pharmakol. 201:161-171, 1943.

696. Ward, J. C. and D. G. Crabtree. Strychnine X. Comparative Accuracies of Stomach Tube and Intraperitoneal Injection Methods of Bioassay. J. Amer. pharm. Ass., sci. Ed. 31: 113-115, 1942.

697. Poe, C. F., et al. Toxicity of Strychnine for Male and Female Rats of Different Ages. J. Pharmacol. exp. Ther. 58:239-242, 1936.

698. Leroy, J. G. and A. F. de Schaepdryver. Catecholamine Levels of Brain and Heart in Mice after Iproniazid Syrosingopine and 10-Methoxydeserpidine. Arch. int. Pharmacodyn. 130:231-234, 1961.

699. Garattini, S., et al. Reserpine Derivatives with Specific Hypotensive or Sedative Activity. Nature (Lond.) 183:1273-1274, 1959.

700. Orlans, F. G. H., et al. Pharmacological Consequences of the Selective Release of Peripheral Norepinephrine by Syrosingopine (SU 3119). J. Pharmacol. exp. Ther. 128: 131-139, 1960.

701. Cook, L. and E. Weidley. Effects of a Series of Psychopharmacological Agents on Isolated Induced Attack Behavior in Mice. Fed. Proc. 19:22, 1960.

702. Heise, G. A. Behavioral Analysis of Tetrabenazine in Animals. Dis. nerv. Syst. 21: (Suppl.) 111-114, 1960.

703. Pletscher, A. Release of 5-Hydroxytryptamine by Benzoquinolizine Derivatives with Sedative Action. Science 126:507, 1957.

704. Astrom, A. and N. H. Persson. The Toxicity of Some Local Anesthetics after Application on Different Mucous Membranes and its Relation to Anesthetic Action on the Nasal Mucosa of the Rabbit. J. Pharmacol. exp. Ther. 132:87-90, 1961.

705. Eichholtz, F. and G. Hoppe. The Convulsive Action of Local Anesthetics and the Effect of Mineral Salts and Adrenaline. Arch. exp. Path. Pharmakol. 173:687-696, 1933.

706. Randall, L. O., et al. The Ganglionic Blocking Action of Thiophanium Derivatives. J. Pharmacol. exp. Ther. 97:48-59, 1949.

707. Hunt, R. and R. R. Renshaw. On Some Effects of Arsonium, Stibonium, Phosphonium and Sulfonium Compounds on the Autonomic Nervous System. J. Pharmacol. exp. Ther. 25:315-355, 1925.

708. Acheson, G. H. and G. K. Moe. The Action of Tetraethylammonium Ion on the Mammalian Circulation. J. Pharmacol. exp. Ther. 87: 220-236, 1946.

709. Acheson, G. H. and G. K. Moe. Some Effects of Tetraethyl Ammonium on the Mammalian Heart. J. Pharmacol. exp. Ther. 84:189-195, 1945.

710. Jodlbauer, A. The Action of Tetramethylammonium Chloride. Arch. int. Pharmacodyn. 7:183-202, 1900.

711. Kuhn, W. L. and E. F. Van Maanen. Effects of Thalidomide on Central Nervous System Drugs. Fed. Proc. 19:264, 1960.

712. Martindale, K., et al. The Effect of Thalidomide in Experimental Gastric Ulcers. J. Pharm. and Pharmacol. 12:153T-158T, 1960.

713. Robinson, M. H. The Effect of Different Intravenous Injection Rates upon the AD_{50}, LD_{50} and Anesthetic Duration of Pentothal in Mice, and Strength-Duration Curves of Depression. J. Pharmacol. exp. Ther. 85: 176-191, 1945.

714. Carmichael, E. B. The Median Lethal Dose (LD_{50}) of Pentothal Sodium for Both Young and Old Guinea Pigs and Rats. Anesthesiology 8:589-593, 1947.

715. Hart, R. The Toxicity and Analgetic Potency of Salicylamide and Certain of its Derivatives as Compared with Established Analgetic-Antipyretic Drugs. J. Pharmacol. exp. Ther. 89:205-209, 1947.

716. Irwin, R. L., et al. The Activity of Certain Lycoramine Derivatives on Muscle. J. Pharmacol. exp. Ther. 134:53-59, 1961.

717. Somjen, G. G. and M. Gill. The Mechanism of the Blockade of Synaptic Transmission in the Mammalian Spinal Cord by Diethyl Ether and by Thiopental. J. Pharmacol. exp. Ther. 140:19-30, 1963.

718. Hey, P. and G. L. Willey. Choline 2: 6-Xylyl Ether Bromide; an Active Quaternary Local Anesthetic. Brit. J. Pharmacol. 9: 471-475, 1954.

719. Nasmyth, P. A. and W. H. H. Andrews. The Antagonism of Cocaine to the Action of Choline 2, 6-Xylyl Ether Bromide at Sympathetic Nerve Endings. Brit. J. Pharmacol. 14:477-483, 1959.

720. McLean, R. A., et al. A Series of 2, 6-Disubstituted Phenoxylethyl Ammonium Bromides with True Sympathomimetic Properties. J. Pharmacol. exp. Ther. 129:11-16, 1960.

721. Coupland, R. E. and K. A. Exley. Effects of Choline 2:6 Xylyl Ether Bromide upon the Suprarenal Medulla of the Rat. Brit. J. Pharmacol. 12:306-311, 1957.

722. McLean, R. A., et al. Pharmacology of Trimethyl (2-(2, 6-Dimethylphenoxy) Propyl)-Trimethylammonium Chloride, Monohydrate; Compound 6890 or β-TM10. J. Pharmacol. exp. Ther. 129:17-23, 1960.

723. Everett, G. M., et al. Tremor Induced by Tremorine and its Antagonism by Anti-Parkinson Drugs. Science 124:79, 1956.

724. Everett, G. M., et al. Production of Tremor and a Parkinson-Like Syndrome by 1-4 Dipyrrolidino-2-Butyne, "Tremorine." Fed. Proc. 15:420-421, 1956.

725. Kaelber, W. W. and R. E. Correll. Cortical and Subcortical Electrical Effects of Psychopharmacologic and Tremor-Producing Compounds. Arch. Neurol. Psychiat. (Chic.) 80:544-553, 1958.

726. Korol, B. and L. Soffer. Cardiovascular Activity of D- and L-Octopamine. Pharmacologist 5:247, 1963.

727. Barlow, O. W. Reactions of the Rat to Avertin Crystals, Avertin Fluid and Amylene Hydrate. Arch. Surg. 26:689-695, 1933.

728. Burtner, R. R. and G. Lehmann. The Hypnotic Properties of Some Derivatives of Trihalogenated Alcohols. J. Pharmacol. exp. Ther. 63:183-192, 1938.

729. Barnes, T. C. Relationship of Chemical Structure to Central Nervous System Effects of Tranquilizing and Anticonvulsant Drugs. J. Amer. pharm. Ass., sci. Ed. 49:415-417, 1960.

730. Tedeschi, D. H., et al. The Neuropharmacology of Trifluoperazine: a Potent Psychotherapeutic Agent. Arch. int. Pharmacodyn. 122:129-143, 1957.

731. Richards, R. K. and G. M. Everett. Tridione: A New Anticonvulsant Drug. J. Lab. clin. Med. 31:1330-1336, 1946.

732. Hoppe, J. O. and A. M. Lands. The Toxicologic Properties of N, N-Dimethyl-N'(3-Thenyl-N' (2-Pyridyl) Ethylenediamine Hydrochloride (Thenfadil): A New Antihistamine Drug. J. Pharmacol. exp. Ther. 97:371-378, 1949.

733. Macri, F. V. Curare-Like Activity of Some Bis-Fluorenyl-Bis-Quaternary Ammonium Compounds. Proc. Soc. exp. Biol. (N. Y.) 85: 603-606, 1954.

734. Berger, F. M. and R. P. Schwartz. The Toxicity and Muscular Effect of d-Tubocurarine Combined with β-Erythroidine, Myanesin or Evipal. J. Pharmacol. exp. Ther. 93:362-367, 1948.

735. Marsh, D. F. and M. H. Pelletier. Curariform Activity of Quaternary Ammonium Iodides Derived from Cinchona Alkaloids. J. Pharmacol. exp. Ther. 92:127-130, 1948.

736. Everett, G. M. Pharmacological Studies of d-Tubocurarine and Other Curare Fractions. J. Pharmacol. exp. Ther. 92:236-248, 1948.

737. Barbour, H. G. and L. L. Maurer. Tyramine as a Morphine Antagonist. J. Pharmacol. exp. Ther. 15:305-330, 1920.

738. Kuntzman, R. and M. Jacobson. Depletion of Heart Norepinephrine by Tyramine. Pharmacologist 5:258, 1963.

739. Nasmyth, P. A. In: Ciba Foundation Symposium, p. 337, eds. Vane, J. R., et al. Little Brown, Boston, 1960.

740. Egami, M. A Pharmacological Study of Afferent Impulse from the Small Intestine. Jap. J. Pharmacol. 4:160-167, 1955.

741. Barer, G. R. and E. Nusser. Cardiac Output during Excitation of Chemo-Reflexes in the Cat. Brit. J. Pharmacol. 13:372-377, 1958.

742. Benforado, J. M., et al. Studies on Veratrum Alkaloids. XXIX. The Action of Some Germine Esters and of Veratridine upon Blood Pressure, Heart Rate and Femoral Blood Flow in the Dog. J. Pharmacol. exp. Ther. 130:311-320, 1960.

743. Hagen, E. C. and J. L. Radomski. The Toxicity of 3-(Acetonylbenzyl)-4-Hydroxycoumarin (Warfarin) to Laboratory Animals. J. Am. pharm. Ass. 42:379-382, 1953.

744. Preziosi, P., et al. On the Pulmonary and Cardiovascular Effects of Warfarin Sodium. Arch. int. Pharmacodyn. 123:227-238, 1959.

745. Röthlin, E. and R. Hamet. On the Toxicity and Adrenolytic Activity of Pseudocorynathine Compared with That of Corynanthine and Yohimbine. Arch. int. Pharmacodyn. 50:241-250, 1935.

746. Barrett, E., et al. A Comparison of the Activity of Various Adrenolytic Agents in Antagonizing the Epinephrine Potentiation Induced by Ganglionic Blockage. J. Pharmacol. exp. Ther. 110:3-4, 1954.

747. McCubbin, J. W. and I. Page. Do Ganglionic Blocking Agents and Reserpine Affect Central Vasomotor Activity? Circ. Res. 6:816-824, 1958.

748. Nasmyth, P. A. An Investigation of the Action of Tyramine and its Interrelationship with the Effects of Other Sympathomimetic Amines. Brit. J. Pharmacol. 18:65-75, 1962.

749. György, L. and M. Dóda. Adrenaline Tachyphylaxis after Dibenamine. Arch. int. Pharmacodyn. 124:66-75, 1960.

750. Riker, W. K. and A. Komalahiranya. Observations on the Frequency Dependence of Sympathetic Ganglionic Blockade. J. Pharmacol. exp. Ther. 137:267-274, 1962.

751. Melville, K. I. Studies on the Cardiovascular Actions of Chlorpromazine. I. Antiadrenergic and Antifibrillatory Actions. Arch. int. Pharmacodyn. 115:278-305, 1958.

752. Ross, J., Jr., et al. The Influence of Intracardiac Baroreceptors on Venous Return, Systemic Vascular Volume and Peripheral Resistance. J. Clin. Inves. 40:563-572, 1961.

753. Byck, R. The Effect of C_6 on the Carotid Chemoreceptor Response to Nicotine and Cyanide. Brit. J. Pharmacol. 16:15-22, 1961.

754. Lamond, D. R. and C. W. Emmens. The Effect of Hypophysectomy on the Mouse Uterine Response to Gonadotrophins. J. Endocrin. 18:251-261, 1959.

755. Boccabella, A. V. Reinitiation and Restoration of Spermatogenesis with Testosterone Propionate and Other Hormones after a Long-Term Post-hypophysectomy Regression Period. Endocrinology 72:787-798, 1963.

756. Smith, B. D. and J. T. Bradburg. Ovarian Weight Response to Varying Doses of Estrogens in Intact and Hypophysectomized Rats. Proc. Sec. exp. Biol. (N. Y.) 107:946-949, 1961.

757. Fain, J. N. and A. E. Wilhelmi. Effects of Adrenalectomy, Hypophysectomy, Growth Hormone and Thyroxine on Fatty Acid Synthesis in vivo. Endocrinology 71:541-548, 1962.

758. Nejad, N. S., et al. Hormonal Repair of Defective Lipogenesis from Glucose in the Liver of the Hypophysectomized Rat. Endocrinology 71:107-112, 1962.

759. Meineke, H. A. and R. C. Crafts. Correlation Between Oxygen Consumption and Erythropoiesis in Hypophysectomized Rats Treated with Various Doses of Thyroxine. Proc. Soc. exp. Biol. (N. Y.) 102:121-124, 1959.

760. Evans, E. S., et al. Erythropoietic Response to Calorigenic Hormones. Endocrinology 68: 517-532, 1961.

761. Baker, B. L. Elevation of Proteolytic Activity in the Pancreas of Hypophysectomized Rats by Hormonal Therapy. Proc. Soc. Biol. (N. Y.) 108:238-242, 1961.

762. De Bodo, R. C. and M. W. Sinkoff. The Role of Growth Hormone in Carbohydrate Metabolism. Ann. N. Y. Acad. Sci. 57:23-60, 1953.

763. Wick, A. N., et al. Effect of 11-Desoxycorticosterone Acetate upon Carbohydrate Utilization by the Depancreatized Rat. Proc. Soc. exp. Biol. (N. Y.) 71:445-446, 1949.

764. Scow, R. O., et al. Effect of Hypophysectomy on the Insulin Requirement and Response to Fasting of "Totally" Pancreatectomized Rats. Endocrinology 61:380-391, 1957.

765. Allegretti, N. Gamma-Globulin Concentration in Normal and Depancreatized Rats Subjected to Formalin Stress. Arch. int. Pharmacodyn. 93:367-372, 1953.

766. Ingle, D. J., et al. Comparison of the Effect of 11-ketoprogesterone, 11α-Hydroxyprogesterone and 11β-Hydroxyprogesterone upon the Glycosuria of the Partially Depancreatized Rat. Endocrinology 53:221-225, 1953.

767. Ingle, D. J. Effect of 11-Desoxycorticosterone Acetate on the Glycosuria of Partially Depancreatized Rats. Proc. Soc. exp. Biol. (N. Y.) 69:329-330, 1948.

768. Greeley, P. O. The Action of Insulin as Indicated by Depancreatized Herbivora. Am. J. Physiol. 150:46-51, 1947.

769. Gastaldi, F. Glycemic Changes Caused by Testosterone Propionate in Normal and Pancreatectomized Dogs. Studi Sassaresi 25: 601-606, 1947.

770. Gillman, J. The Relationship of Hyperglycemia to Hyperlipemia and Ketonaemia in Depancreatized Baboons (Papio Ursinus). J. Endocrin. 17:349-362, 1958.

771. Glasser, S. R. and J. L. Izzo. The Influence of Adrenalectomy on the Metabolic Actions of Glucogon in the Fasting Rat. Endocrinology 70:54-61, 1962.

772. Gross, F. and P. Lichtlen. Experimental Renal Hypertension: Renal Content of Kidneys in Intact and Adrenalectomized Rats Given Cortexone. Am. J. Physiol. 195:543-548, 1958.

773. Smith, S., et al. Some Metabolic Effects of Diethylstilbestrol and Deoxycorticosterone Acetate in Adrenalectomized and Intact Male Rats. Proc. West. Va. Acad. Sci. 32:22-25, 1960.

774. Pores, G. Effects of Aldosterone on Carbohydrate Metabolism of Normal and Adrenalectomized Rats. C. R. Soc. Biol. (Paris) 155: 790-792, 1961.

775. Hungerford, G. F. Effect of Adrenalectomy and Hydrocortisone on Lymph Glucose in Rats. Proc. Soc. exp. Biol. (N. Y.) 100:754-756, 1959.

776. Pederson-Bjergaard, K. and M. Tonnesen. The Effects of Steroid Hormones on Muscular Activity in Rats. Acta endocrinal 17: 329-337, 1954.

777. Aterman, K. Cortisol and Spermiogenesis. Acta endocrinal 22:371-378, 1956.

778. Fain, J. N. Effects of Dexamethasone and Growth Hormone on Fatty Acid Mobilization and Glucose Utilization in Adrenalectomized Rats. Endocrinology 71:633-635, 1962.

779. Peres, G. and G. Zwingelstein. Action of Aldosterone on the Blood Proteins of the Normal and Adrenalectomized Rat. J. physiol. (Paris) 53:444-446, 1961.

780. Peters, G. Distribution of Water and Electrolytes in the Organism in Normal and Adrenalectomized, Untreated Rats or Such Rats Treated with Adrenocortical Hormone, and the Influence of Large Oral Water Loads. Arch. exp. Pathol. Pharmakol. 237:119-150, 1959.

781. Winter, H., et al. Antibody Formation in the Adrenalectomized Rat and the Effect of Cortisone. Inter. Arch. Allergy Appl. Immunol. 19:360-376, 1961.

782. Kahlson, G. and S. Renvall. Atrophy of Salivary Gland Following Adrenalectomy or Hypophysectomy and the Effect of Deoxycorticosterone in Cats. Acta physiol. scand. 37: 150-158, 1956.

783. Sesso, A. and R. Migliorini. Nucleic Acid Content and Amylase Activity in the Pancreas of the Rat Following Adrenalectomy and Cortisone Administration. Acta physiol. lat.-amer. 9:5-12, 1959.

784. Gross, F. and H. Haefeli. The Activity of Deoxycorticosterone, Cortisone, and Antihistamine Substances on the Anaphylactic Shock of Adrenalectomized Guinea Pigs. Intern. Arch. Allergy Appl. Immunol. 3:44-53, 1952.

785. Berlin, R. D., et al. Abrupt Changes of Water and Sodium Excretion in Normal and Adrenalectomized Dogs. Am. J. Physiol. 199:275-280, 1960.

786. Daane, T. A. and W. R. Lyons. Effect of Estrone, Progesterone, and Pituitary Mammotropin on the Mammary Glands of Castrated C_3H Male Mice. Endocrinology 55: 191-199, 1954.

787. Kitay, J. T. Pituitary-Adrenal Function in the Rat after Gonadectomy and Gonadol Hormone Replacement. Endocrinology 73:253-260, 1963.

788. Meli, A. Route of Administration as a Factor Influencing the Biological Activity of Certain Androgens and their Corresponding 3-Cyclopentyl Enol Ethers. Endocrinology 72: 715-719, 1963.

789. Rudolph, G. G. and W. R. Starnes. Effect of Castration and Testosterone Administration on Seminal Vesicles and Prostates of Rats. Am. J. Physiol. 179:415-418, 1954.

790. Mandel, P., et al. Effect of Testosterone on the Calcium Balance in the Rat. C. R. Acad. Sci. (Paris) 148:713-715, 1954.

791. Kanai, T. Effect of Androgen on Fine Structure of the Prostate of Castrated Rats. II. The Effect of Administration of Small Doses of Testosterone 3 Days After Castration. Tohoku J. Exptl. Med. 75:309-318, 1961.

792. Levey, H. A. and C. M. Szego. Effects of Castration and Androgen Administration on Metabolic Characteristics of the Guinea Pig Seminal Vesicle. Am. J. Physiol. 183:371-376, 1955.

793. Dagradi, A. and G. Peronato. Influence of the Gonads on Carbohydrate Metabolism. Patol. sper. chir. 1:420-429, 1953.

794. Grunt, J. A. Exogenous Androgen and Nondirected Hyperexcitability in Castrated Male Guinea Pigs. Proc. Soc. exp. Biol. (N.Y.) 85: 540-542, 1954.

795. Munford, R. E. The Effect of Cortisol Acetate on Estrone-Induced Mammary Gland Growth in Immature Ovariectomized Albino Mice. J. Endocrin. 16:72-79, 1957.

796. Grosvenor, C. E. Effects of Estrogen upon Thyroidal I^{131} Release and Excretion of Thyroxine in Ovariectomized Rats. Endocrinology 70:673-678, 1962.

797. Lerner, J., et al. Pregnancy Maintenance in Ovariectomized Rats with 16α, 17α Dihydroxyprogesterone Derivatives and Other Progestogens. Endocrinology 70:283-287, 1962.

798. Woolley, D. E. and P. S. Timiras. The Gonad-Brain Relationship: Effects of Female

Sex Hormones on Electroshock Convulsions in the Rat. Endocrinology 72:196-209, 1963.

799. Escobar del Rey, F. and G. Morreale de Escobar. Studies on the Peripheral Disappearance of Thyroid Hormone. Acta endocrin. 29:161-175, 1958.

800. Barker, S. B., et al. Metabolic Effects of Thyroxine Injected into Normal, Thiouracil-Treated, and Thyroidectomized Rats. Endocrinology 45:624-627, 1949.

801. Halmi, N. S., et al. Improved Intravenous Glucose Tolerance in Thyroidectomized or Hypophysectomized Rats Treated with Triiodothyronine. Endocrinology 64:618-621, 1959.

802. De Bastiani, G., et al. Significance of the Thyrotropic Hormone of the Hypophysis in the Syndrome Resulting from Thyroidectomy. Boll. soc. ital. biol. sper. 32:200-204, 1956.

803. Von Berswordt-Wallrabe, R. and C. W. Turner. Successful Replacement Therapy in Lactating Thyro-parathyroidectomized Rats. Proc. soc. exp. Biol. (N. Y.) 104:113-116, 1960.

804. Harrison, R. G. and T. J. Barnett. Production of Arthritis in Thyroparathyroidectomized Rat by Injections of Deoxycorticosterone Acetate. Ann. rheum. Dis. 12:275-282, 1953.

805. Cramer, C. F. Participation of Parathyroid Glands in Control of Calcium Absorption in Dogs. Endocrinology 72:192-196, 1963.

806. Gordon, A. H. The Parathyroid Hormone. Congr. intern. biochim., Resumes communs, 2e Congr. Paris:53-54, 1952.

807. Talmage, R. V., et al. Effect of Parathyroid Extract and Phosphate Salts on Renal Calcium and Phosphate Excretion after Parathyroidectomy. Proc. soc. exp. Biol. (N. Y.) 88:600-604, 1955.

808. Laron, Z., et al. Phosphaturic Effect of Cortisone in Normal and Parathyroidectomized Rats. Proc. soc. exp. Biol. (N.Y.) 96:649-651, 1957.

809. Page, I. H. and J. W. McCubbin. Effect of Pentobarbital and Atropine on Arterial Pressure Response to Ganglion Blocking Agents. Am. J. Physiol. 194:597-600, 1958.

810. Costa, E., et al. Interactions between Reserpine, Chlorpromazine, and Imipramine. Experientia (Basel) 16:461-463, 1960.

811. Crout, J. R. Inhibition of Catechol-O-Methyl Transferase by Pyrogallol in the Rat. Biochem. Pharmacol. 6:47-50, 1961.

812. Finkleman, B. On the Nature of Inhibition in the Intestines. J. Physiol. (Lond.) 70:145-157, 1930.

813. Chorover, S. L. Effects of Mescaline and Chlorpromazine on Two Aspects of Locomotor Activity in Rats. Fed. Proc. 19:22, 1960.

814. Freyburger, W. A., et al. The Pharmacology of 5-Hydroxytryptamine (Serotonin). J. Pharmacol. exp. Ther. 105:80-86, 1952.

815. Gutman, J. and M. Chaimovitz. The Effect of Anesthetics on Blood Pressure Response to Pain. Arch. int. Pharmacodyn. 137:40-48, 1962.

816. Millar, R. A., et al. Plasma, Adrenaline and Noradrenaline after Phenoxybenzamine Administration, and During Haemorrhagic Hypotension, in Normal and Adrenalectomized Dogs. Brit. J. Pharmacol. 14:9-13, 1959.

817. Walker, H. A., et al. The Effect of 1-Hydrazinophthalazine (C-5968) and Related Compounds on the Cardiovascular System of Dogs. J. Pharmacol. exp. Ther. 101:368-378, 1951.

818. Haury, V. G. and M. E. Drake. The Effect of Intravenous Injections of Sodium Diphenyl Hydantoinate (Dilantin) on Respiration, Blood Pressure, and the Vagus Nerve. J. Pharmacol. exp. Ther. 68:36-40, 1940.

819. Drake, M. E., V. G. Haury, and C. M. Gruber: The Action of Sodium Diphenyl Hydantoinate (Dilantin) on the Excised and Intact Uterus. Arch. int. Pharmacodyn. 43:288-291, 1939.

INDEX

The following information is presented to illustrate the magnitude and scope of the index.

(1) Indexing of Drug Names: Each drug appearing in the main body of the handbook is indexed under its official name and, whenever possible, under three common names. For example, the pages where dosage information can be found for chlorpromazine are listed next to chlorpromazine, Largactil, Thorazine, and Megaphen.

(2) Indexing of Drug Responses: The page numbers, for each drug listed in the main body of the text, will also be found next to each pharmacological action that has been included for the particular drug. For example, the page numbers referring to chlorpromazine will appear next to: anticonvulsant, antiserotonin (*in vitro*), behavior, cardiovascular, decrease spontaneous motor neuron activity, EEG, Lagendorff (*in vitro*), potentiate barbiturate sleep, rabbit atria (*in vitro*), sedative, sympatholytic.

INDEX

mg/kg		Mouse	Rat	Guinea Pig	Rabbit	Cat	Dog	Monkey	
Lethal Dose Y–LD_{50} Z–MLD	IV								
	IP								
	IM								
	SC								
	PO								
	IV								
	IP								
	IM								
	SC								
	PO								
	IV								
	IP								
	IM								
	SC								
	PO								
	IV								
	IP								
	IM								
	SC								
	PO								

IN VITRO

mg %	Cardiac	Vascular	Gut	Uterine	Visceral	Skeletal		

mg/kg		Mouse	Rat	Guinea Pig	Rabbit	Cat	Dog	Monkey	
Lethal Dose Y–LD_{50} Z–MLD	IV								
	IP								
	IM								
	SC								
	PO								
	IV								
	IP								
	IM								
	SC								
	PO								
	IV								
	IP								
	IM								
	SC								
	PO								
	IV								
	IP								
	IM								
	SC								
	PO								

IN VITRO

mg %	Cardiac	Vascular	Gut	Uterine	Visceral	Skeletal		

mg/kg		Mouse	Rat	Guinea Pig	Rabbit	Cat	Dog	Monkey	
Lethal Dose Y–LD_{50} Z–MLD	IV								
	IP								
	IM								
	SC								
	PO								
	IV								
	IP								
	IM								
	SC								
	PO								
	IV								
	IP								
	IM								
	SC								
	PO								
	IV								
	IP								
	IM								
	SC								
	PO								

IN VITRO

mg %	Cardiac	Vascular	Gut	Uterine	Visceral	Skeletal		

mg/kg		Mouse	Rat	Guinea Pig	Rabbit	Cat	Dog	Monkey	
Lethal Dose Y—LD_{50} Z—MLD	IV								
	IP								
	IM								
	SC								
	PO								
	IV								
	IP								
	IM								
	SC								
	PO								
	IV								
	IP								
	IM								
	SC								
	PO								
	IV								
	IP								
	IM								
	SC								
	PO								

IN VITRO

mg %	Cardiac	Vascular	Gut	Uterine	Visceral	Skeletal		

mg/kg		Mouse	Rat	Guinea Pig	Rabbit	Cat	Dog	Monkey	
Lethal Dose Y-LD_{50} Z-MLD	IV								
	IP								
	IM								
	SC								
	PO								
	IV								
	IP								
	IM								
	SC								
	PO								
	IV								
	IP								
	IM								
	SC								
	PO								
	IV								
	IP								
	IM								
	SC								
	PO								

IN VITRO

mg %	Cardiac	Vascular	Gut	Uterine	Visceral	Skeletal		

mg/kg		Mouse	Rat	Guinea Pig	Rabbit	Cat	Dog	Monkey	
Lethal Dose Y–LD_{50} Z–MLD	IV								
	IP								
	IM								
	SC								
	PO								
	IV								
	IP								
	IM								
	SC								
	PO								
	IV								
	IP								
	IM								
	SC								
	PO								
	IV								
	IP								
	IM								
	SC								
	PO								

IN VITRO

mg %	Cardiac	Vascular	Gut	Uterine	Visceral	Skeletal		

mg/kg		Mouse	Rat	Guinea Pig	Rabbit	Cat	Dog	Monkey	
Lethal Dose Y-LD_{50} Z-MLD	IV								
	IP								
	IM								
	SC								
	PO								
	IV								
	IP								
	IM								
	SC								
	PO								
	IV								
	IP								
	IM								
	SC								
	PO								
	IV								
	IP								
	IM								
	SC								
	PO								

IN VITRO

mg %	Cardiac	Vascular	Gut	Uterine	Visceral	Skeletal		

mg/kg		Mouse	Rat	Guinea Pig	Rabbit	Cat	Dog	Monkey	
Lethal Dose Y—LD_{50} Z—MLD	IV								
	IP								
	IM								
	SC								
	PO								
	IV								
	IP								
	IM								
	SC								
	PO								
	IV								
	IP								
	IM								
	SC								
	PO								
	IV								
	IP								
	IM								
	SC								
	PO								

IN VITRO

mg %	Cardiac	Vascular	Gut	Uterine	Visceral	Skeletal		

mg/kg		Mouse	Rat	Guinea Pig	Rabbit	Cat	Dog	Monkey	
Lethal Dose Y–LD_{50} Z–MLD	IV								
	IP								
	IM								
	SC								
	PO								
	IV								
	IP								
	IM								
	SC								
	PO								
	IV								
	IP								
	IM								
	SC								
	PO								
	IV								
	IP								
	IM								
	SC								
	PO								

IN VITRO

mg %	Cardiac	Vascular	Gut	Uterine	Visceral	Skeletal		

mg/kg		Mouse	Rat	Guinea Pig	Rabbit	Cat	Dog	Monkey	
Lethal Dose Y–LD_{50} Z–MLD	IV								
	IP								
	IM								
	SC								
	PO								
	IV								
	IP								
	IM								
	SC								
	PO								
	IV								
	IP								
	IM								
	SC								
	PO								
	IV								
	IP								
	IM								
	SC								
	PO								

IN VITRO

mg %	Cardiac	Vascular	Gut	Uterine	Visceral	Skeletal		

mg/kg		Mouse	Rat	Guinea Pig	Rabbit	Cat	Dog	Monkey	
Lethal Dose Y – LD_{50} Z – MLD	IV								
	IP								
	IM								
	SC								
	PO								
	IV								
	IP								
	IM								
	SC								
	PO								
	IV								
	IP								
	IM								
	SC								
	PO								
	IV								
	IP								
	IM								
	SC								
	PO								

IN VITRO

mg %	Cardiac	Vascular	Gut	Uterine	Visceral	Skeletal		

mg/kg		Mouse	Rat	Guinea Pig	Rabbit	Cat	Dog	Monkey	
Lethal Dose Y–LD_{50} Z–MLD	IV								
	IP								
	IM								
	SC								
	PO								
	IV								
	IP								
	IM								
	SC								
	PO								
	IV								
	IP								
	IM								
	SC								
	PO								
	IV								
	IP								
	IM								
	SC								
	PO								

IN VITRO

mg %	Cardiac	Vascular	Gut	Uterine	Visceral	Skeletal		

mg/kg		Mouse	Rat	Guinea Pig	Rabbit	Cat	Dog	Monkey	
Lethal Dose Y–LD_{50} Z–MLD	IV								
	IP								
	IM								
	SC								
	PO								
	IV								
	IP								
	IM								
	SC								
	PO								
	IV								
	IP								
	IM								
	SC								
	PO								
	IV								
	IP								
	IM								
	SC								
	PO								

IN VITRO

mg %	Cardiac	Vascular	Gut	Uterine	Visceral	Skeletal		

mg/kg		Mouse	Rat	Guinea Pig	Rabbit	Cat	Dog	Monkey	
Lethal Dose Y—LD_{50} Z—MLD	IV								
	IP								
	IM								
	SC								
	PO								
	IV								
	IP								
	IM								
	SC								
	PO								
	IV								
	IP								
	IM								
	SC								
	PO								
	IV								
	IP								
	IM								
	SC								
	PO								

IN VITRO

mg %	Cardiac	Vascular	Gut	Uterine	Visceral	Skeletal		